Radio Listener's Guide

by
William Barden, Jr.

Radio Shack

A Division of Tandy Corporation

First Edition
First Printing—1987

Library of Congress Catalog Card Number: XX-XXXXX

Table of Contents

Section I
World of the BBC, Radio Moscow, Police Calls, Aircraft Communications, and Hams

Section II
Radio Equipment

Section III. Glossary of Terms

Section IV. Appendices

Preface

Radio is a lot more than "Rockin' EZ on the Big 100" or "All News on Radio 73". In addition to broadcasting your favorite rock or Bach, news, radio psychologist talk shows, and stock market quotations, radio can also mean these things:

- exciting police and fire calls
- news direct from Moscow or Paris
- listening in on clandestine "spy" communications
- hearing computer communications between radio "hams"
- following the progress of aircraft flights as they land at local airports, or even monitoring flights thousands of miles away
- free weather maps direct from satellites in earth orbit

The thrilling thing about these events is that you can be a part of them for very little investment in equipment. Today's radios are very sophisticated and surprisingly inexpensive.

A shortwave receiver priced at less than $100 at your local Radio Shack store is far superior to one that cost hundreds of dollars more a few years ago and will allow you to listen in to the world.

A $200 scanner radio provides monitoring of police, fire, and amateur radio channels that bring you armchair close to exciting real-world events as they are happening.

For about the same price as the scanner you can buy a complete Citizen's Band transmitter and receiver combination to allow you to talk to local CBers.

For about the same price, or a little more, you can purchase a communications receiver. This type of receiver can not only receive shortwave broadcasts from foreign broadcasters, but can also receive Morse code and other interesting types of transmissions.

For $400 to $1000 you can buy an amateur radio transceiver. With a little effort you can obtain a ham license that will enable you to make contacts with other hams world wide, even within the Eastern Block countries.

In this book we'll try to explain away a lot of the mystique about radio communications and show you how easy it is to listen to exciting and interesting radio events. We'll explain how radio works in simple terms, and about the various types of radio broadcasts and transmissions. We'll provide a list of radio bands and describe the stations and transmissions you're liable to find there. We'll then describe the various types of radio equipment— portable shortwave receivers, CB gear, scanners, and amateur radio equipment—and give you some tips on what to look for when buying it. We'll also provide a glossary of radio "buzzwords" to help you understand the jargon of radio communications.

Radio offers something for everyone—news buffs, foreign language students, pilots, experimenters, and electronics hobbyists—read about what it will offer you in the following pages!

Chapter 1.
Radio — What is It?

A lot of people know only about two radio-frequency bands on radio equipment—AM and FM. The AM and FM bands are the two bands allocated in the United States for commercial broadcasting stations to provide voice and music entertainment programs for the general public. In fact, there are many more bands available. The AM and FM broadcast bands occupy only about 1/50th of the total radio space currently being used for broadcasting! To understand where those "hidden" bands are, what they are used for, and how to receive them, we have to look at a few basic concepts— nothing very complicated, however.

Generating Radio Waves

Just what do we mean by a "frequency band", anyway? Think of a guitar string. If you pluck the string, it vibrates back and forth to cause the sound waves that are picked up by your ear. The shorter the string, the faster the string vibrates and the higher the sound.

The guitar string sound can also be produced by an electrical current traveling through a wire to a speaker. Here, instead of a vibrating string, the current flows first in one direction and then in the other. An A above middle C played on a guitar vibrates at 440 cycles per second. "Cycles" here means the same thing as a mechanical vibration —a reversal of current. The current flows in one direction and then in the opposite direction. If the electrical current to the speaker reverses itself 440 times per second, an A above middle C note will sound from the speaker as well.

Now suppose that the current in the wire to the speaker reverses itself faster and faster—1000 times per second, 5000 times per second, 10,000 times per second, and higher. As the reversals, or *frequency,* of the current increases, strange things began to happen. The electrical current creates an electromagnetic *field* around the wire. A compass brought near the wire will be affected by the magnetic effects of this field. Some of the energy involved in causing current flow through the wire radiates into space as radio waves, detectable at some distance from the source. This effect is heightened by an *antenna* that is designed for the frequency involved.

The frequency of reversals is measured in a term called *hertz,* which simple means the number of complete cycles or reversals per second. The vibrating guitar string, for example, has a frequency of 440 cycles per second, or 440 hertz. The abbreviation for hertz is "Hz", and we'll be using it throughout this book.

The Radio Spectrum

The frequency of electrical circuits which generate radio waves goes from low frequencies such as the audible A above middle C to much greater frequencies—up to 3,000,000,000,000 Hz or so. At that point, the type of wave generated is infrared light! For practical purposes, though, most radio transmission uses frequencies from about 30,000 Hz on up to about 1,000,000,000 Hz. Those are the frequencies we'll cover in this book, for those are the frequencies for which inexpensive radio equipment is available. By the way, the term "radio" is an old term that encompasses many types of transmissions in this band of frequencies. Television is just another form of radio wave emission.

The radio-frequency spectrum is divided into "bands" of frequencies just to make it more convenient for discussion. The bands are shown in Table 1-1.

Table 1-1. Radio-Frequency Bands

30 - 300 Hz	Extremely low frequencies	ELF
300 - 3 kHz	Voice frequency	VF
3 - 30 kHz	Very low frequencies	VLF
30 - 300 kHz	Low frequencies	LF
300 - 3000 kHz	Medium frequencies	MF
3 - 30 MHz	High frequencies	HF
30 - 300 MHz	Very high frequencies	VHF
300 - 3000 MHz	Ultrahigh frequencies	UHF
3 - 30 GHz	Super high frequencies	SHF
30 - 300 GHz	Extremely high frequencies	EHF

The abbreviation kHz in the table stands for "thousand Hz", so a 3-kHz frequency is 3000 Hz. The abbreviation "MHz" stands for "one million Hz", so a 3-MHz frequency is 3,000,000 Hz. The abbreviation "GHz" stands for "one billion Hz", so 3 GHz frequency is 3,000,000,000 Hz. It's a lot more convenient to use the abbreviations than to write out all the zeroes involved! The two terms most used in this book are kHz and MHz, for 1000 Hz and 1,000,000 Hz, respectively.

Radio Equipment and Frequencies

Generally, it's easier to make radio equipment that operates at lower frequencies. When the frequencies start to get into the VHF frequencies 30 MHz and above, radio equipment becomes more elaborate. As the frequency *increases,* the length of radio waves *decrease.* A UHF television antenna, for example, is smaller than a VHF television antenna—it's designed to receive the shorter UHF waves. At higher frequencies the radio waves become so short that they are large compared to such things as the diameter of tubing used in antennas. A 3-kHz wave is about 328,000 feet long, for example, a 3-MHz wave is 328 feet long, and a 3-GHz wave is 0.32 feet long!

Band Use

Just to give you a flavor of what the various bands are used for, here's a brief description—we'll discuss the bands in detail later in the book.

VLF - There's not much equipment available for these low frequencies. However, they are used for submarine and other military communications

LF - These frequencies are used for beacons (such as navigational markers), by commercial stations for messages, by time and standard stations, and for European "long-wave" broadcasting. There is not a great deal that can be heard in the United States on these frequencies.

MF - The AM broadcast band starts at the low end of this band of frequencies and ends in the middle. Also used in Europe and around the world. The higher portions are used by tropical short-wave stations, the military, amateurs, and commercial stations. Plenty of activity and crowded bands above the AM broadcast band. Generally communications from several hundred to several thousand miles.

HF - A very crowded part of the spectrum, used by shortwave stations, commercial stations, amateurs, military, aircraft, marine, secret U.S. and foreign broadcasters, Citizen's Band, and others. Everything from weather maps to voice to code and teleprinter is carried. Long-range communications (world wide).

VHF - These frequencies are not very good for other than short range (several hundred miles). However, the band is very crowded with police, fire, emergency services, military, the FM band, aircraft communications, the lower numbered television channels, amateur, commercial services, and others.

UHF - Line-of-sight communications only. Not as crowded as VHF, but becoming so. UHF television, amateur, commercial use, Citizen's Band, cellular radio and car phones, and others.

How Radio Waves Travel

You can see from the chart above that each band is used for different purposes. One of the chief reasons for this is the way radio waves travel around the earth. This is called radio wave *propagation.*

Radio wave travel is really by two waves (see Figure 1-1). One of the waves is called the *ground wave* and generally follows the surface of the earth, gradually diminishing in strength. Depending upon the frequency involved, ground wave communications are good for several hundred miles at best.

The second type of wave is called the sky wave. The *sky* wave radiates out at an angle to the horizon. Depending upon the frequency, radio waves may be reflected by different layers of the earth's *ionosphere*. This is actually many layers of ionized (electrically charged) particles that circle the earth at altitudes of 60 to 200 miles. At VHF frequencies and above, radio waves tend *not* to be reflected by the earth's ionosphere—they simply pass through it into space and continue forever, gradually getting weaker and weaker. At lower frequencies, including the MF and HF bands, radio waves may be reflected back to earth. We say "may be" here because the ionosphere is very much affected by the amount of sun's radiation. The more radiation received from the sun, the more the ionosphere is charged.

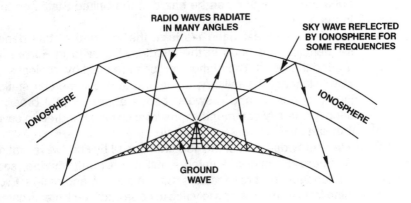

Figure 1-1.
Radio Wave Travel

During daylight hours, the sun charges the ionosphere. During nightime hours, this ionization decreases. Low-angle radio signals in the MF band (below 3 MHz) are absorbed by one of the layers in the ionosphere during daylight hours, as shown in Figure 1-2). Higher-angle radio waves are reflected back to earth, but reach only locations closer to the radio wave source. During daylight hours, therefore, the MF bands are good only for short distance communication. In evening hours, however, the lower-angle radio waves are absorbed less and reflected back to earth over greater distances, as much as halfway around the world.

Radio waves in the HF band (3 MHz to about 30 MHz) are absorbed less at low angles than the MF bands and can therefore provide long-distance daytime communications by reflection from the ionosphere. This reflection is also called "skip". The greater the frequency, the greater this distance will be, up to a point. A station transmitting at 6 MHz, for example, can probably be heard for 500 miles during the day and around the world at night. A station transmitting at 14 MHz can probably be heard around the world during daylight hours, with diminishing distance at night. Stations at higher frequencies in the HF band are more variable—reception depends upon a variety of factors.

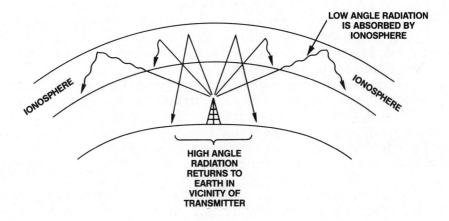

Figure 1-2.
MF Band and the Daylight
Ionosphere

One of those factors is the sunspot cycle. Sunspots are dark areas on the surface of the sun (see Figure 1-3). The number of sunspots change in a pattern of 11 years, the 11-year sunspot cycle. More sunspots signal more active solar radiation and greater ionization of the ionosphere. When the sunspot activity is high, frequencies in the upper end of the HF band are usable world wide, offering such excellent propagation that even very low-power transmitters (such as CB radios) can be heard around the world. When the sunspot activity is low, the upper end of the HF bands appear to be almost "dead"—only the strongest signals are heard, and at times nothing can be heard.

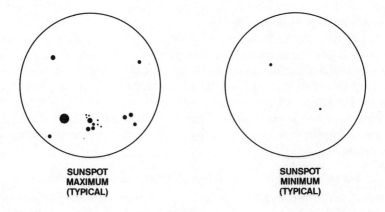

SUNSPOT
MAXIMUM
(TYPICAL)

SUNSPOT
MINIMUM
(TYPICAL)

Figure 1-3.
Sunspots

Another factor affecting radio wave propagation is the amount of solar activity. Solar flares, brief periods of high-intensity solar activity, can not only make it dangerous for astronauts, but can also knock out radio communications over many radio bands for days at a time.

Although there are exceptions, radio stations above 30 MHz are generally used for "line-of-sight" communications, such things as local television and FM radio. Even these applications, though, are affected by unusual propagation conditions. It is possible to receive television stations from across the United States or internationally, given a good antenna, the right conditions, and a local television station that has "signed off" for the evening.

Some unusual factors affect propagation in the VHF and UHF region. The ionosphere is not that constant, and can be "patchy" providing short periods of long-distance VHF communication. *Aurora* propagation can provide short periods during the aurora borealis when VHF signals can cover long distances. Even brief periods of ionization created by meteors can result in long-distance communication in the VHF or UHF radio bands.

Stations operating at and above the VHF bands are a mixed blessing. Although long-distance communication cannot be reliably done, the line-of-sight aspect permits local communications without interference from other parts of the world.

The propagation characteristics of the radio bands, then, are one of the chief determiners of the bands' use. However, there's another way band use is determined. An international radio conference meets periodically to determine the band allocations. This conference is made up of representatives of most of the countries of the world who agree on what frequencies should be used and by whom. If this were not the case, the bands would become even more crowded than they are!

Radio Licenses and Listening

Inside the United States, the Federal Communications Commission (FCC) allocates licenses for radio and television communication. No license is needed for listening to broadcasts in any part of the radio spectrum. In the strictest interpretation of a 50-year old Communications Act, you cannot divulge the contents of any conversation you may hear over a radio. However, this law has never been enforced against transgressions of casual listeners or hobbyists. It was intended to protect business or commercial user's privacy.

The Electronics Communication Privacy Act of 1986

However, a new law, the Electronic Communications Privacy Act of 1986 (the ECPA) protects "encrypted" radio communications—transmissions that are purposely scrambled for privacy. Unless you build a decoder box such as those sold to decode scrambled telecasting, there is no problem in monitoring any band in that regard. Also protected, however, are *subcarriers, common-carrier* transmissions, *studio-to-transmitter links, private microwave,* and *remote broadcast pickups.*

Subcarriers carry audio or other information as a subordinate part of a normal transmission—a telecast that includes a secondary audio in a foreign language uses a subcarrier. Unless the subcarrier is decoded with special equipment, this also poses no problem to the casual listener.

Common-carrier transmissions may pose a problem. This term refers to phone companies transmitting to mobile car phones or to voice pagers. Evidently some of the lobbying for the ECPA was done by the Mobile Communications industry. The best advice that can be given is to not intentionally monitor cellular car phones in the 800-MHz region or mobile communications in general, although monitoring portable phone transmissions and radiotelephone transmissions in the marine or aviation band is permissible.

Private microwave links also do not pose a problem with the equipment described in this book, as microwaves start at about 1,000,000,000 (1 GHz) and require special equipment.

Remote broadcast pickups and studio-to-transmitter links refer to such transmissions as television network coverage via radio—"Now we take you to Joe Newsreeder on the scene". Monitoring of this type of transmission has been exempted from penalties as long as there is no devious purpose in the eavesdropping.

This is a recent law and has not been clearly defined. However, it appears that as long as you monitor transmissions that are "readily accessible to the general public" and stay away from common-carrier mobile communications there should be no problem on any frequency from 0 to 512 MHz and above.

Private Conversations

About private conversations: There are a number of bands in which you can eavesdrop on radiotelephone or even neighborhood portable phones. Many of the users are not aware that their conversations can be monitored. At times, listening to such conversations can be quite embarrassing. Therefore, liberal amounts of the Golden Rule should be used on monitoring certain radio transmissions.

Operating a Radio Transmitter

Although no license is required for *listening* to any radio transmission, there is *always* a license required for operating a radio transmitter, unless that transmitter is very low power. These licenses are granted by the FCC to private individuals and companies. The type of licenses range from easy to obtain Citizen's Band licenses to the competitive licenses for AM/FM bands and television broadcasting.

In spite of licensing requirements in the U.S. and world-wide, every country has numerous clandestine radio stations, ranging from guerrilla armies and drug traffickers to pranksters and unlicensed Citizen's Band operators. While we don't advise starting your own pirate radio, these transmissions are fun to listen to in many cases, and can be exciting as well. The author has personally heard drug-related deals going down (as they say in television series) via radio.

Subbands and Channels

The bands described earlier in this chapter are really just convenient slices of the radio spectrum. (They each start at three to a power of ten so that the radio wavelengths come out to even numbers in the metric system— a radio broadcast at 3 MHz, for example, has a wavelength of 100 meters). Allocations of frequencies are made in smaller slices. As examples, a popular shortwave band is 9.5 to 9.9 MHz. Another band is the amateur radio "two-meter" band at 144 to 148 MHz.

Within these subbands, there are sometimes channels. Channels are similar to the channels used in television broadcasting. When television signals are broadcast, they require a width of about 5 MHz. This bandwidth determines the number of channels that can be packed into a given band. Here are the first five television channels and their frequency assignments:

Channel 2	54 to 60 MHz
Channel 3	60 to 66 MHz
Channel 4	66 to 72 MHz
Channel 5	76 to 82 MHz
Channel 6	82 to 88 MHz

Normal voice communication requires a bandwidth of about 6 kHz (6000 Hz), so at higher frequencies, such as shortwave bands, many more channels can be packed into the band. In the Citizen's Band of frequencies from 26.965 to 27.405 MHz, for example, there are 40 channels, each occupying about 10 kHz (10,000 Hz), and numbered from 1 to 40. The numbering of these channels does not necessarily follow increasing frequencies, by the way, but in many cases does. Allocation by channels is found primarily at VHF frequencies and above. It's just a convenient way to slice up the radio spectrum—it's much easier to remember channel 23 than 27.255 MHz! Figure 1-4 shows a typical band, subband, and channel.

Radio Equipment

It is possible to receive radio broadcasts in an improperly filled tooth! However, the next simplest radio receiver is more reliable. Take a cardboard paper roll, wind two layers of insulated wire around it, add an electronic part called a diode, another called a variable capacitor, and an inexpensive headphone—parts available at any Radio Shack store—and voila! there's a

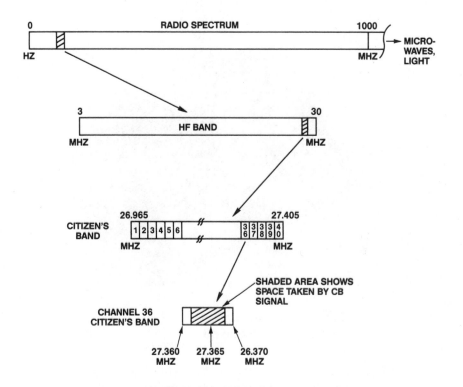

Figure 1-4.
Bands, Subbands, and Channels

working radio receiver. Surprisingly, such a receiver can receive world-wide broadcasts! Radio Shack also carries a number of simple radio kits, a little bit more complicated than a crystal radio, but not that much. They make an excellent introductory radio kit for youngsters (see Figure 1-5).

The "crystal set" receiver was the norm for radios of 80 years ago. Today's receivers use the same basic principles and a few others to accomplish a similar goal. There are several types of radios available from Radio Shack and other sources. These, by the way, are covered in more detail in the second section of the book. We'll give you a preview here, however. Not included are the garden variety AM and FM receivers.

- Shortwave receivers. These are inexpensive ($50 to $400) radio receivers designed to receive the standard AM and FM bands and also popular shortwave bands for foreign broadcast stations in the MF and HF regions.
- Communication receivers. These are more elaborate receivers that can receive not only foreign broadcast stations, but code and specialized communications as well. From $200 to $800.

Figure 1-5.
Radio Kit

- VHF continuous tuning receivers. These are radio receivers that tune the VHF band to receive police, fire, emergency, and aviation radio, in addition to the FM band.
- Citizen's Band Transceivers. These are both radio receivers and trans-mitters. You can not only listen to broadcasts, but reply on Citizen's Band frequencies as well. A CB license requires only an application.
- Weather radios. These are simple receivers that receive only NOAA weather broadcasts on VHF frequencies.
- Amateur Radio Transceivers. These are both radio receivers and transmitters that operate on amateur radio frequencies. Usually there are two types, those that operate on HF bands and those that operate on VHF and UHF bands. An amateur radio license is required for transmission.
- Scanners. These are VHF or VHF/UHF receivers that operate differently from the continuous tuning VHF receivers. A set of channels can be programmed so that the receiver continuously scans the channels several times a second. If a station transmits on one of the programmed channels, the receiver stops and allows you to listen to the station. Scanning takes place again after the station ends its transmission. A neat piece of equipment that allows monitoring of radio transmission between two broadcasters on different channels without having to rapidly switch manually back and forth between them.

Chapter 2
Types of Broadcasting

There's an incredible variety of information going out over radio broadcasts. The obvious things we think of immediately are voice and music over the AM/FM broadcast bands and television video and audio over television channels. However, there are dozens more types of broadcasting in wide use today. We'll cover the more common ones in this chapter.

Voice Communication

Voice communication is used from about 148 kHz on up. The reason it is not used on lower frequencies in the LF and VLF bands is that voice communication requires about 5 kHz for one channel—this is a large percentage of the band! However, at the top end of the LF band and above, voice is the most popular form of communication, both in the form of one-way broadcasts, such as foreign shortwave stations, and two-way transmissions, such as emergency services.

The usual *mode* of voice communication is identical to the broadcasting done on the AM broadcast band, from 525 kHz to 1.605 MHz. This form of broadcasting is called "AM" for *amplitude modulation*—the radio signal occupies about 10 kHz but actually contains only half the usable frequencies—about 5 kHz (see Figure 2-1). If you're an audio buff you'll know that 5 kHz is not a very good frequency response, and that's why shortwave broadcasts sound very much like telephone conversations. The high frequencies are purposely cut off so that the broadcast occupies less space in the crowded bands.

AM broadcasts are used on all frequencies up to about 30 MHz and can be received by simple equipment, much like a normal AM radio, but with extended frequency coverage.

Another mode of voice communication used in the MF and HF bands is called *single sideband* (SSB). In this mode of broadcasting, only half the width is required—about 5 kHz, allowing more channels in the crowded bands. In AM broadcasting, much of the energy for a radio signal goes into the carrier frequency for the signal. In addition, as shown in Figure 2-1, there are two sidebands that carry the same audio information, where only one would do the trick. Single-sideband transmissions filter out one of the sidebands and the carrier frequency, allowing only one sideband to be transmitted, at half the width, as shown in Figure 2-2.

However, there is a catch! Without a special receiver using a circuit called a *BFO* or *beat frequency oscillator*, SSB stations sound like Donald

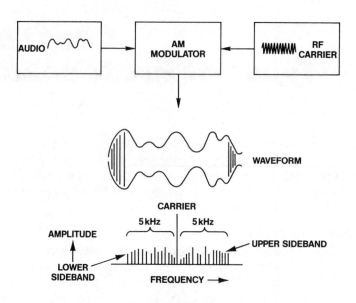

Figure 2-1.
Amplitude Modulation Transmission

Duck. The BFO effectively reinserts the carrier to make the transmission sound like a normal AM broadcast, or nearly so. SSB transmission is widely used by amateurs, the military, and commercial stations for voice communication because it is able to "punch through" over longer distances. It is also used by some Citizen's Band stations. However, hardly any shortwave broadcasters currently use it.

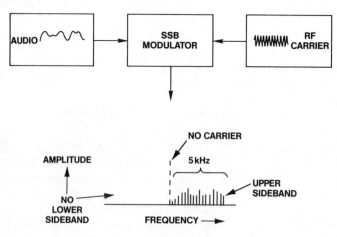

Figure 2-2.
Single-Sideband Transmission

Another popular mode of voice communication is "FM", or "frequency modulation", shown in Figure 2-3. FM is characterized by a bandwidth of about 6 to 180 kHz, depending upon the band and fidelity required (television FM audio is about 80 kHz). It is much more immune to atmospheric noise than AM, and for that reason is used for music stations in the FM broadcast band. It is also used extensively in the VHF bands and above—virtually all police, fire, emergency service, and amateur transmission in these bands is FM. FM radio equipment is very common, but a little more sophisticated then the equipment used in lower-frequency bands. There's no special operating skill required to use FM equipment, however, as you can see from using FM receivers for the FM broadcast band (88 MHz to 108 MHz).

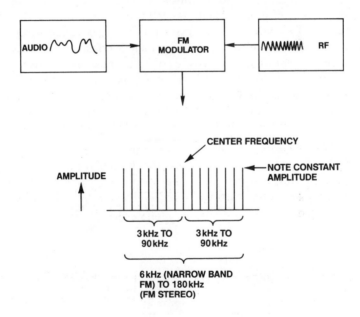

Figure 2-3.
Frequency Modulation Transmission

A type of FM called *narrow-band FM* (NBFM) is also used in the HF bands and above. This type of FM has a much narrower bandwidth than wide-band FM—more consistent with bandwidth requirements in the crowded HF band.

Code Transmission

International Morse Code transmission has been used since the earliest days of radio. The code sounds very much like the examples you've heard in television and movies. Code was used initially because it could be received and decoded at much longer distances than voice transmission. Code is still used today for that very reason, although not as extensively as in the past. There's also a number of code enthusiasts among the ranks of radio amateurs — you'll find most code transmission in HF in the crowded amateur bands.

Code, or "CW" ("continuous wave"), transmissions can be received only by a receiver with a beat frequency oscillator (BFO) circuit. Unfortunately, many shortwave receivers do not provide this capability. On a receiver without a BFO, you'll hear only a thumping or hissing during code transmission, which you may be able to follow in some cases.

The International Morse Code has patterns based upon the frequency of use of the alphabet, digits, and special characters in normal English text. The letter "e" is the most frequent letter in English text, and is assigned a "dot", a single unit of sound. The letter "t", the second most frequent letter, uses a "dash", a sound that is three times as long as a dot. The letter "a", used less frequently than an "e" or "t", is assigned a dot dash combination. Other letters use other combinations based upon their frequency of use. The letter "q", for example, is seldom used and is assigned a longer sequence — dash dash dot dash. Appendix II lists common characters of the International Morse Code. A Morse Code Transmission is shown in Figure 2-4.

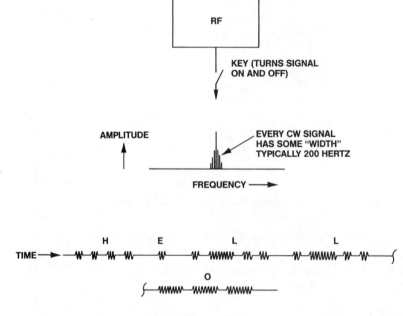

Figure 2-4.
Morse Code Transmission

Code is sent with a "key" and code operators are known as "brass-pounders". Some military code operators can listen to a 60-word-per-minute code transmission and type the message at the same time, pausing occasionally to sip at their coffee. To most of us, this would sound like an unintelligible buzz!

Among amateurs, small computers have often replaced code keys. Characters are now typed on computer keyboards and the computer generates the proper sequence of dots and dashes. The computer also reads the incoming code and translates it into characters on the computer's screen.

Teleprinter Transmission

Another mode of communication in widespread use is radio *teleprinter*, commonly called RTTY. This communication method is somewhat similar to Morse Code, but at higher speeds. Whereas most code operation is done at speeds of about ten to 50 words per minute, radio teleprinters can operate at speeds of 60 to 1200 words per minute or more. An RTTY device used to look much like an office typewriter on a stand. These days, however, the computer has replaced much of the older equipment and an RTTY station usually looks like a computer terminal keyboard and a central computer.

RTTY transmissions can be received with inexpensive equipment and radio amateurs communicate world-wide by this communication method. Again, however, reception in the MF and HF bands requires a receiver with a BFO. An RTTY transmission can best be described as a high-speed "deedle-deedle-deedle" with occasional periods of constant tone or signal. An RTTY transmission is illustrated in Figure 2-5.

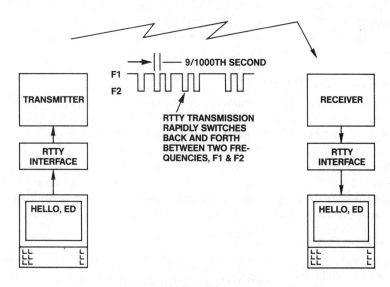

Figure 2-5.
RTTY Transmission

There are several variations of RTTY used by amateurs. One is called *AMTOR*, Amateur Teleprinting Over Radio. In AMTOR, the transmissions have a built-in error checking capability. If an error in transmission has been detected, the short transmission is repeated. *Packet radio* uses a similar scheme to ensure error-free transmissions in the VHF and UHF region.

AMTOR can be recognized by a "chirp-chirp-chirp" sound and can be heard on ham and other bands.

Facsimile Transmission

Another type of radio transmission is radio facsimile, or fax, as it is sometimes called. The purpose of fax is to transmit a picture or photo over radio. Obviously, you can do this with television transmission in an instant, but don't forget two factors: Television bandwidth requirements mean that television must be used on VHF or UHF bands and above and these bands are only line-of-sight. Fax is used to transmit over hundreds or thousands of miles on the HF band. But how?

Facsimile transmission involves scanning the picture to be transmitted a line at a time. Imagine putting the picture in a typewriter and rolling it up line by line. The information on one line is sent, the paper is rolled up another line and the next line is sent, and so forth. Rather than transmitting the entire picture as a series of dots in 1/30th of a second, as in normal TV, the picture is sent over minutes and reassembled by a light beam that shines on a piece of photo paper on the receiving end in pace with the transmitting station.

Facsimile transmissions sound like a continuous buzzing signal. NOAA (the government weather service) uses facsimile to transmit weather maps on MF and HF bands. News photos (wire photos) are sent as well.

Facsimile transmission is shown in Figure 2-6.

Slow-Scan Television

Another mode of communication similar to facsimile is *slow-scan* television, used by radio amateurs on the MF and HF amateur bands (see Figure 2-7). Because the bandwidth of a normal television picture is too great, a slow-scan television process breaks the television picture up into 120 lines and sends a line at a time, just as in facsimile. The entire process takes about eight seconds. The receiving station does not produce a photographic image of the transmitted picture as in facsimile, but builds up an image in a computer buffer, which is then displayed.

Fast-Scan Television

Fast-scan television refers to the normal television found on channels 2 through 13 (VHF) and 14 through 83 (UHF) or to amateur fast-scan television. Here a picture is sent in 1/30th of a second and the channel is about 5 MHz wide, about 1/6 of the total radio spectrum from 0 hertz up to 30 MHz!

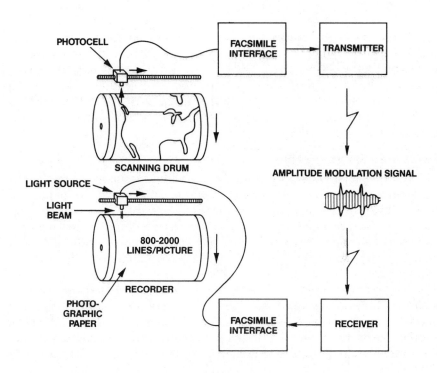

Figure 2-6.
Facsimile Transmission

Fast-scan television is also used by radio amateurs on the 420- to 440- and 1240- to 1294-MHz ham bands.

Television signals are quite complex and require a great deal of electronics to decode the video and audio information. The audio portion of a television signal is actually sent as FM, and can be received by an inexpensive FM receiver that tunes the television audio channels.

Some radio listeners (television watchers?) watch for television band conditions that permit reception of long distance television signals. A good antenna system helps with this. "DX" (distant) television reception from hundreds or even thousands of miles away is possible with patience and the right propagation conditions.

If you live in a major city, you're probably familiar with pay television stations that send out a specially encoded television signal that is decoded by users with decoding boxes. These transmissions appear garbled without the decoding, but otherwise the television process is essentially the same. Cable television, another way of receiving fast-scan television, really does not operate "over the air" as the signal does not radiate. It is contained within the coaxial cable that is used to send the signal over miles of local

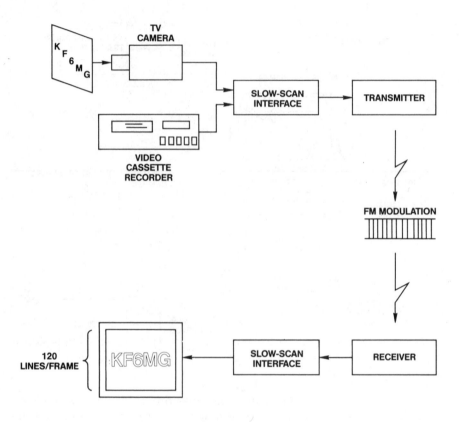

Figure 2-7.
Slow-Scan Television Transmission

territory. Special amplifiers are used to boost the signal strength every thousand feet or so.

Repeaters

Radio repeaters are a special form of VHF and UHF communication, primarily in the amateur bands. If you hear a a number of people communicating over the same VHF or UHF channel, and all signals are the same strength, a repeater is probably being used (see Figure 2-8).

A repeater is a remote radio station, usually situated on a mountaintop or hill. A transmitting station, using low power, transmits to the repeater on one frequency, which rebroadcasts the signal at high power and over a wider range on another frequency. Operators alternate on transmissions, allowing many people to use the same repeater, each one seizing control for his transmission.

There are literally thousands of repeaters across the United States, Europe, and other countries. Each repeater serves a local community. By

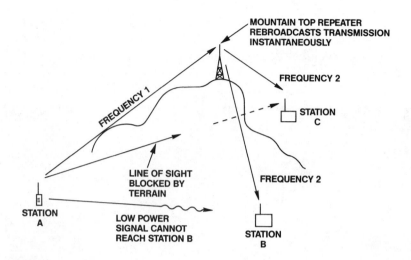

Figure 2-8.
Repeater Operation

using special networks, radio amateurs are able to link repeaters for voice or computer communications and transmit messages hundreds of miles.

Portable Phones

The portable phone has become a popular household and office item. Portable phones use two different frequencies, one for transmission and one for reception, typically 46 MHz and 49 MHz. Transmissions are sent "in the clear" so that anyone with a receiver covering the frequencies can listen in. (Let's stress once again that there's no law against listening to such conversations, if that's what you like to do, but that there is a law against divulging the contents of the conversation to others.)

Car phones usually operate in the 150-MHz band and are easy to find. Local marine transmissions from commercial or private ships are also found in the 160-MHz region of the VHF band.

Satellite Reception

One of the most interesting aspects of radio in recent times is the use of satellites to transmit original data or relay signals. There are hundreds of satellites currently in orbit, some top secret and some specifically placed in orbit to provide useful information.

Some of the latter type are the NOAA weather satellites. These satellites continuously map the earth by visible light or infared photography and then send the pictures back to earth in the VHF or UHF bands. The picture is assembled at the receiving station by facsimile or video means. You don't need to be a radio amateur to receive these transmissions on the VHF band,

and many have built the necessary equipment to reproduce the weather maps from a combination of off-the-shelf or surplus receiving equipment and simple mechanical/photographic devices or small computers (see Figure 2-9).

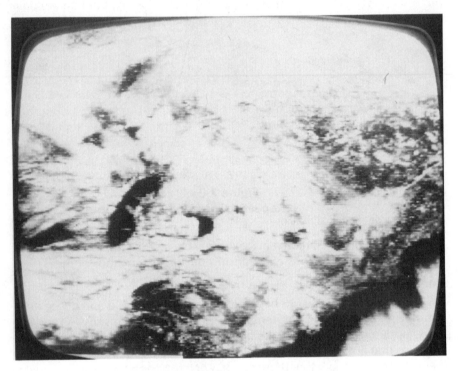

Figure 2-9.
Soviet Meteor Weather Satellite Picture
Courtesy of Dr. Ralph E. Taggart

The amateur radio community has also been active in satellite communications. The first amateur radio satellite was launched in 1961. OSCAR I sent a continuous "HI" in Morse code as it circled the globe. Since then, dozens of other amateur radio satellites have been launched from the United States, the Soviet Union, and Japan with much more extensive capabilities.

Current amateur satellites receive VHF or UHF transmissions and rebroadcast them on command around the globe. Several astronauts are also amateurs as well and have spent time in Space Shuttle orbit communicating with earth-bound stations on VHF amateur bands. Some of these transmissions can be received with ordinary scanners found at Radio Shack stores and a little planning. NASA communications are also available on the VHF and UHF bands, although not all operate in the FM mode.

Even if you are not a ham, it is possible to monitor the the amateur radio satellites for "beacon" information on the HF, VHF, and UHF bands.

Of course, there are also satellites that are used by such services as HBO and WTBS. These transmissions can be received by TVRO (television receive only) satellite dishes that can be seen across the country, but that are quite expensive (at least $1000) and require more elaborate equipment than most of the receivers in this book.

Transmitting Power

Transmitting power refers to the amount of energy sent to the antenna in a given time. The greater the amount of energy, the stronger will be the received signal. A radio transmitter's signal not only depends upon how much power the transmitter uses from the electric company's mains (or its own generator), though. It also depends upon the *effective radiated power*— how much power is radiated by the antenna of the station. Depending upon the type of transmission, the antenna may make the transmitter output very directional—it may be "beamed" in a certain direction. In other cases, the transmitter output will be evenly distributed in all directions.

Transmitter power varies from a few hundred milliwatts, such as used in children's walkie-talkies, to the two-million watt transmitter used at station NAA in Maine by the U.S. Navy. Typical low-power AM broadcasters are 1 kW (1000 watts) and higher-power AM broadcasters are 10 kW. The larger foreign broadcasters use 100 to 250 kW transmitters.

Chapter 3
Shortwave Broadcasters

Why do countries broadcast? In the United States, the answer in most cases is to make money from advertising. However, shortwave broadcasters do not carry advertising. Or do they? One form of advertising is propaganda. Radio Moscow and the Voice of America both carry their own answers to world political questions. Other countries also represent their point of view, which may differ quite markedly from the perspective found in the United States. That's one reason for shortwave broadcasting.

Another reason countries use shortwave broadcasting is as a means to communicate with their citizenry. Many countries, especially the developing ones, use shortwave broadcasting as a means of communicating news, sports, education, and entertainment to their people, who may be spread over a wide area. These countries do not have the means nor the budget to have individual radio stations in every small town, as in the United States.

Frequency Assignments

Frequency assignments for broadcasting are regulated by international agreement. The current frequency allocations for broadcasting are shown in Table 3-1.

Table 3-1. Foreign Broadcast Bands

LW	148.5 - 283.5 kHz	European stations*
MW	526.5 - 1606.5	Europe, Middle East, Africa, Asia; North, Central, and South America
120	2.300 - 2.498 MHz	Tropical broadcasting
90	3.200 - 3.400	Tropical broadcasting
75	3.900 - 4.000	World-wide broadcasting*
60	4.750 - 5.060	Tropical broadcasting*
49	5.950 - 6.200	World-wide broadcasting
41	7.100 - 7.300	World-wide broadcasting*
31	9.500 - 9.750	World-wide broadcasting
	9.750 - 9.900	World-wide broadcasting*
25	11.650 - 11.700	World-wide broadcasting*
	11.700 - 11.975	World-wide broadcasting
	11.975 - 12.050	World-wide broadcasting*
19	15.100 - 15.450	World-wide broadcasting
	15.450 - 15.600	World-wide broadcasting*

16	17.550 - 17.700	World-wide broadcasting*
	17.700 - 17.900	World-wide broadcasting
13	21.450 - 21.750	World-wide broadcasting
	21.750 - 21.850	World-wide broadcasting*
11	25.670 - 26.100	World-wide broadcasting

The first column in the table shows the band designation in meters. The second column shows the frequency assignments. The last column shows the type of broadcasting service. An asterisk marks those bands that are shared with other services.

The European Long-Wave Band

The first set of frequency assignments is the long-wave band. This set of frequencies (148.4 - 283.5 kHz) is used in Europe for stations similar to our AM broadcast band—local news, sports, and entertainment. However, it is shared with radio navigation services and mobile services to a certain extent. These stations cannot usually be heard during the day, but occasionally can be heard during evening hours in the Eastern United States.

The AM Broadcast Band

The next set of frequencies (526.5—1606.5 kHz) is the familiar AM broadcast band. In Europe, this band is referred to as medium wave. This band is used by many countries, as you can see from the table. The reason that you cannot hear the other countries normally is that local United States stations override longer-distance signals.

Occasionally you've probably heard stations from Mexico or Canada while tuning between local stations. A good time for looking for distant stations is in the evening, when long distances can be covered by stations operating in these frequencies. Local stations may also be off during evening hours. Even local stations that are on 24 hours a day occasionally turn off their transmitter for "maintenance". During this period (usually early morning hours), you may be able to log a foreign station.

Tropical Broadcasting

The shortwave bands below 5.950 MHz are know as tropical broadcasting bands. These frequencies are used in tropical countries, which have an unusually high number of thunderstorms compared to other parts of the world. Thunderstorms cause crashing static bursts. Because of this, tropical countries are allocated frequencies which are quieter than shortwave frequencies, and these frequencies normally have less atmospheric noise. Another reason for special consideration of these frequencies is that a single low-power transmitter may serve a region about 120 miles in every direction around the transmitter (primarily at night). Developing countries again do not have the resources for the super-powered transmitters of countries such as Great Britain or France.

The ranges of stations operating in these bands is generally 450 miles during daylight hours and a thousand miles or more during evening hours. Because many stations are low power, reception may be more difficult than in other broadcasting bands.

49- and 41-Meter Bands

These two bands are among the most popular shortwave bands and are used almost as much as all other shortwave bands combined. Countries use these bands not only for international broadcasts, but for broadcasts on national levels as well. Depending upon the radio propagation conditions, the bands are usable during both daylight and evening hours.

31- and 25-Meter Bands

These are the next most popular shortwave bands. They are good for daylight hour reception during the entire year with ranges of up to thousands of miles. During the evening, world-wide reception is possible.

Above the 25-Meter Band

These bands are not as reliable as the lower-frequency shortwave bands. The reason for this is that these frequencies are subject to varying propagation conditions caused by the sunspot cycle and other factors. Conversely, though, at times these bands offer excellent reception with extremely strong signals. Most broadcasters limit their use of these frequencies, although they may shift to the frequencies when band conditions are good.

A Typical Listening Session

The following notes represent a merger of several typical listening sessions on the shortwave bands on the West Coast of the United States. Your own listening will probably be similar, unless you happen to be caught in a period of unusually bad radio propagation.

All of the stations were received on a moderately priced communications receiver. Most of the stations were also received at the same time on an under $100 shortwave receiver. The signal levels refer to an S-meter signal level on the communications receiver. An S1 reading is very low, while an S9 is very strong. The scale is also calibrated above the S9 mark with ten and 20 db (decibels) over S9, indicating an extremely strong signal.

Frequencies are in MHz.

5.905:   Radio Moscow. Same program as 6.150 in English. Switched to Russian language at midnight. Signal level S5 - S6.

5.985:   Voice of Free China, Taipai, Taiwan, Republic of China. Program in English including singing and language lessons. Signal level S6-S7. 11:00 pm.

6.000:   Radio Moscow, North American Service. Classical music. Signal level S5—S7. 5:00 pm.

6.005: BBC World Service. News in English. Signal level S5 - S7. 5:00 pm.

6.040: Radio Deutsch Welle, Voice of Germany. German language broadcast with German songs. Signal level S5 - S7. 5:00 pm.

6.090: Radio Habana Cuba. Spanish language broadcast. Signal from S3 -S7. 5:00 pm.

6.150: Radio Moscow. Discussion of what Radio Moscow termed "the anti-Soviet" film "Amerika". CIA chief William Casey linked with production. Followed by a discussion of "Soviet Life". All in English. Signal level S4 to S5. Midnight.

9.525: Radio Havana Cuba. News in English. Among the headlines was this one: "U.S. ready to Invade Nicaragua". Signal level S6.

9.590: Radio Norway International. News in English. Signal level S5. 8:00 am.

9.640: BBC World Service. News in English read by Francis Lyons. Signal level constant at S7.

9.655: Radio Australia. "Ethics in Medical Research" program in English. Radio Australia can be easily identified during breaks by "Waltzing Matilda" theme. 23:00 (11 pm). Signal S2, just above noise.

9.695: Radio Japan. News in English. Signal level S7. 8:00 am.

9.715: Radio Netherlands. News in English followed by a broadcast of classical music. 20 db over S9 signal. 10:00 pm.

9.740: BBC World Service. 8:00 am.

11.830: USA religious broadcast (probably WYFR—Family Radio, Florida). In English. Signal level S3 with high noise level. 11:00 am.

11.840: Radio Moscow. In English. S5 signal level. 11:00 am.

11.930: Spanish language broadcast to Cuba(?). Signal level S6. 11:00 am.

13.665: Radio Moscow, North American service. Reading of letters from Canadian and United States citizens supporting Soviet side of nuclear disarmament questions. Many innocent correspondents have found embarrassing editing of some of their replies to Radio Moscow. Signal level S5 - S6. 5:30 pm.

15.260: Radio Canada International was heard here with a strong signal. Radio Canada can be identified by continuous broadcasting of the the first notes of the Canadian national anthem, "O Canada" on the hour mark. In English. 10:00 am.

15.325: Radio Canada again, but this time in a French language broadcast. A weaker signal. 10:00 am.

15.410: Voice of America broadcasting a music program, followed by world news. Extremely strong signal. In English. 10:00 am.

15.570: Radio Netherlands in English broadcasting a news program. Signal varying in strength between S5 and S9. 10:00 am.

15.580: Voice of America again, with the same program as on 15.410 MHz. News broadcast is preceded by the first seven notes of "Yankee Doodle". 10:00 am.

Logging Foreign Stations

There's a lot of excitement and fun in listening to foreign shortwave stations. It's easy to do, in one sense— just turn on the receiver, and there they are! During normal band conditions, there are so many foreign stations on a band like the 31-meter band that one simply follows the other on the dial. Here's a typical list of the frequencies that had stations during a typical listening session:

9.550, 9.575, 9.590, 9.600, 9.605, 9.615, 9.635, 9.640,
9.650, 9.660, 9.670, 9.680, 9.690, 9.700, 9.705, 9.715,
9.725, 9.740, 9.765, 9.775. 9.800, 9.810, 9.815, 9.840

That's 24 stations in just one shortwave band without trying very hard!

You'll find a great deal of variety among the stations. Many foreign broadcasters broadcast in English, beaming their broadcasts to North America during convenient listening hours. They also broadcast in the language of their country. In some cases, the stations broadcast in many languages, beaming their signal to different geographic areas. News, features that describe the culture of the country, radio drama, music, and sports are all to be found among the stations.

On another level, shortwave listening is more of a hobby, rather than casual listening. It's fun to search for that elusive station that you haven't been able to find. While the BBC, Radio Moscow, and Radio Japan are all easy to find, it's a lot more difficult to locate some of the Asian, African, and South American countries. This is especially true when the broadcasts are not in English. Most stations identify themselves on the hour mark, sometimes in English. Another thing to look for is a musical identification. Radio Canada repeats the four notes of the national anthem "O Canada" over and over before the hour mark, for example. Other foreign broadcasters do the same, using a few notes from their anthem or popular songs. Radio Sweden broadcasts varying bird songs at times.

Foreign Broadcast Information

The bible for referencing foreign broadcasters is the "World Radio TV Handbook" (Billboard Ltd.). This is a compendium of all foreign broadcasters with current frequencies and times. It can usually be found at the larger bookstores. Broadcasting information is also available from the broadcasters themselves. Usually, the broadcaster will inform you of the frequencies on which he is currently broadcasting, and on which frequencies he will be broadcasting in English. Broadcasting schedules do change for the season because of the different seasonal propagation characteristics and also to take advantage of the best band conditions.

Times for foreign broadcasts are usually given in UTC UTC times are referenced to Greenwich, England, which leads the United States in the hourly time as follows:

> Pacific Time: UTC—8 hours
> Mountain Time: UTC—7 hours
> Central Time: UTC—6 hours
> Eastern Time: UTC—5 hours

For daylight saving time, add an extra hour to the result. UTC time uses a 24-clock. In the 24-hour clock, 1:00 pm is 13:00 hours, 2:00 pm is 14:00 hours, and so forth, up to 23:59:59 hours, or 11:59:59 pm, one second before midnight. At midnight, the time changes to 00:00:00. When subtracting time, carry over 24 hours. For example, if the UTC time is 04:00, the Pacific Time is 04:00—08:00, or 20:00 of the previous day! If in doubt about the UTC, tune in radio stations WWV or WWVH on 5.000, 10.000, or 15.000 MHz—they give the UTC time every minute, on the minute mark.

QSL Cards

Many shortwave listeners collect proof of reception of foreign broadcasts and many foreign broadcasters are more than happy to send *QSL cards* or some other form of certification to verify such reception. Many of these "QSLs" are quite colorful and interesting. Some broadcasters, though, *do not* encourage QSL cards. Send the particulars of the broadcast received to the address of the station (see the World Radio TV Handbook).

Include the following items in your request:

- Date
- Time (start and end)
- Frequency
- Signal strength and band conditions (SINPO—see below)
- Program content—a brief description of the program heard
- Name and address

The signal strength and band conditions are usually given in a code called the SINPO code, an international standard way of reporting reception. The letters S-I-N-P-O stand for Signal, Interference, Noise, Propagation (fading), and Overall merit. The codes are shown in Table 3-2 below:

Table 3-2. SINPO Codes

S(ignal Strength):	5 Excellent	P(ropagation):	5 None
	4 Good		4 Slight
	3 Fair		3 Moderate
	2 Poor		2 Severe
	1 Barely audible		1 Extreme
I(nterference):	5 None	O(verall merit):	5 Excellent
	4 Slight		4 Good
	3 Moderate		3 Fair
	2 Severe		2 Poor
	1 Extreme		1 Unusable
N(oise):	5 None		
	4 Slight		
	3 Moderate		
	2 Severe		
	1 Extreme		

Remember that the station is interested in an accurate report, so try not to give "5s" to every part of the SINPO report.

To help in getting a reply, send return postage in the form of International Reply Coupons (IRCs), available at any post office.

Some broadcasters also encourage correspondence from listeners. However, it has to be said that stations like Radio Moscow have been known to be selective about the responses read over the air, or even to do some fairly extensive editing of an innocent listener's remarks. On the other hand, most stations are genuinely interested in listeners comments regarding programming and probably happy that their foreign broadcasts are achieving what is at least part of their goal—better international understanding and good will.

Chapter 4
Other Types of Broadcasting in the Lower Frequencies

The foreign broadcast frequency allocations occupy only about 3.5 MHz of the radio spectrum from 15 kHz up to 30 MHz. The remainder of the spectrum is used by all other services. (In addition, some of the shortwave bands share their frequencies with other services, as described in Chapter 2.) Who are the other services? Among the list you'll find airlines, marine operators, wire services, the military, radio amateurs, and probably yourself! In this chapter we'll describe some of these other services.

Transmissions Below the AM Broadcast Band

Besides the European long-wave band (see Chapter 3) there are other types of transmissions below the AM broadcast band, which starts at 550 kHz.

OMEGA is an electronic navigation system developed by the US. Navy for submarine communication, since long-wave transmission can be received underwater. Four frequencies, from 10.2 to 13.6 kHz, are used by six transmitters spaced 6000 miles apart.

LORAN-C is used for Long Range Navigation. It is a world-wide (or nearly so) chain of transmitters that transmit in sequence on 100 kHz. Transmitters are synchronized by an atomic clock. Reception of two stations provides a fix for aircraft or (primarily) ships at sea. LORAN has a pulsating sound.

Radiobeacons are used for navigational purposes by ships at sea and by aircraft. The marine radiobeacons are found between 285 and 325 kHz and can be heard within 20 to 1000 miles of their source, dependent upon the beacon and time of day. The beacons transmit their location in Morse code. The San Francisco Light Buoy, for example, is found at 305 kHz and transmits a slow speed ---/..-. (SF).

Aircraft radiobeacons are found below and above the marine radiobeacons and also transmit in code (Santa Barbara, CA transmits "BA" at 338 kHz, for example.) Aircraft radiobeacons generally have a longer range than the marine radiobeacons—50 miles or more.

Both types of radiobeacons can be heard for long distances under the right band conditions.

The AM Broadcast Band

The AM broadcast band is used not only in the United States and Canada, but in Europe, East Asia and the Pacific, and South America as well. In these countries it is called the medium wave (MW) band. Because of the number of stations in the United States and Canada (over 5000), power is limited in the U.S. to 50 kilowatts (50,000 watts). European stations use considerably more power in some cases.

If it were not for the United States stations, you would be able to copy foreign stations during evening hours when band conditions were favorable. As it stands, however, you can still have fun seeing how many individual stations in the United States, Canada, and Mexico you can copy by scanning the dial and many listeners have received overseas stations as well.

The standard spacing for broadcast band stations is 10 kHz, starting at 540 and continuing to 1600 kHz (1.6 MHz). This 10-kHz separation is not observed world wide, however, and you may hear stations that *heterodyne* United States stations because they are off by several kHz. (A heterodyne is a whistling caused by two frequencies that are slightly off and beat together to generate an audio tone.)

An external antenna or especially a directional broadcast band antenna is a great help in playing the broadcast band DX (distance) game (see Chapter 11).

At a typical listening session on the broadcast band in Orange County, California (near Los Angeles) the following stations were picked up during the evening hours, using a receiver with a built-in telescoping antenna:

KTAR Phoenix, KNBR San Francisco, KFMB San Diego,
WBAP Ft. Worth, KOA Denver, KOMA Oklahoma City,
KFBK Sacramento, CA

WBAP and KOMA are about 1200 miles from the author's location. Receiving stations at greater distances is certainly possible. A book such as "White's Radio Log" (Worldwide Publications) or another that lists all AM stations by frequency and location is a big help in broadcast band "DX'ing". It's very difficult at times to understand whether an announcer is saying "KBXU", "KDSQ", or "KGSU" even with good reception, and a radio reference book will usually solve the problem. Another hint: most stations that start with a "K" are west of the Mississippi, while those that start with a "W" are east of the Mississippi.

Years ago, there were "clear-channel" stations that had one frequency all to themselves. These days, there are still clear-channel stations, but they share the channel with other stations in widely separated areas—Illinois, North Carolina, and Oklahoma, for example. Many times you'll hear several stations at once, the stronger stations superimposed over the weaker. It is sometimes possible, given the right program content, to pick out the weaker station and identify it though the stronger station.

Portable Phones

Portable phones (the type you can walk around with) are low-powered radio transmitters. They operate on two frequencies, one for the base and one for the handset. Older portable phones use base frequencies in the 1.665 to 1.770 MHz range (just above the AM broadcast band) and handset frequencies are in the 49.670 to 49.990 MHz range, just below the 6-meter amateur band. Because of the low power involved, reception is usually not possible beyond a few hundred feet or so with the typical installation.

Some installations, however, use outside antennas to increase the range for farm or ranch operation. It's entirely possible to hear one or both sides of conversations with receivers that tune those frequencies. However, as many of these calls are of a personal or business nature, use the Golden Rule.

MF frequencies used are:

1.665 MHZ
1.690
1.695
1.710
1.725
1.730 ·
1.750
1.755
1.770

Frequencies in the 49-MHz range are given in Chapter 5.

Marine Transmissions

Coast Guard

The frequency of 2.182 MHz is the international emergency frequency for marine communications. Transmissions can be in AM or SSB. Other communications with the U.S. Coast Guard are usually in SSB and found at

Ship(MHz)	Shore (Coast Guard, MHz)
4.1343	4.4287
6.2000	6.5065
8.2415	8.7654
12.3424	13.1132
16.5344	17.3073

Ship-to-Shore Telephone

Various commercial stations, including AT&T, provide ship-to-shore telephone service on the high seas in SSB. Two frequencies are used, one for ship transmission and one for ship reception. Look for these in the 2.0 to 2.6 MHz, 4.0 to 4.4 MHz, 8.2 to 8.8 MHz, 12.3 to 13.2 MHz, 16.4 to 17.3 MHz, and 22.0 to 22.6 MHz areas, depending upon band conditions. The shipboard transmission frequency is usually lower by 400 to 800 kHz.

Also look for NOAA weather service bulletins in the same frequency ranges.

CW Transmissions

CW (code) transmissions are not as common as RTTY transmissions (see below), but they can be found all over the dial. The most common place for CW is on the amateur bands, of course, but we'll exclude the ham bands from the following discussion. Code can be received only by a receiver with a beat frequency oscillator (BFO).

Code can be found from various beacons, such as aircraft or navigational beacons, or from stations that actually communicate with other stations. You're liable to hear most stations when they are just marking the frequency by sending a repetitive pattern of CW followed by a station identification. An example is "V V V V V DE FUF" sent over and over. This typical signal is heard on 4.054 MHz and is a transmission from the Fort de France Naval installation at Martinque, Carribean. The "V" letter is a common code character sent for testing and marking. The "DE" is a CW abbreviation for "from". The "FUF" is the station identifier of the transmitting station. The speed of this transmission is about 13 words per minute, a typical speed. If an actual message is being sent, it will be sent in International Morse at speeds of about 13 to 20 words per minute or more.

It doesn't take too long to learn how to copy CW at 13 words per minute—perhaps 50 hours of practice—but it does take considerably more time to be able to copy 20 words per minute. One possible solution is a small computer system with a code/RTTY interface connected to the audio of the receiver. Such a unit will receive and automatically decode the CW, displaying it on the screen of the computer. A minimum system can be had for as little as $400.

If you opt to learn code for the listening fun of it, however, a good way to do it is to listen to amateur radio station W1AW, the American Radio Relay League's official station. W1AW sends code practice sessions every day on these frequencies:

1.818, 3.58, 7.08, 14.070, 21.08, 28.08, 50.08, and 147.555 MHz

Slow-speed practice is sent 9 am and 7 pm EST or EDST on Mondays, Wednesdays, and Fridays and 4 and 10 pm on the other days of the week. Slow speed is 5, 7 1/2, 10, 13, and 15 words per minute.

Another option is to buy code practice tapes, usually available from dealers that sell amateur radio equipment.

To tune in CW on a receiver with a BFO, switch to the CW (or USB or LSB) function. Then turn the RF gain control down and the AF gain (or AUDIO) up to the loudest level. Now advance the RF gain as CW stations are tuned. This eliminates a mushy-sounding CW tone.

Radio Teleprinter

The radio spectrum up to 30 MHz abounds with radio teleprinter (RTTY) transmissions. These signals cannot be received without a receiver with BFO (a receiver having a function switch with a "CW" or "USB/LSB" setting) as the signals are "unmodulated" and consist only of rapidly turning the transmitter on and off at two frequencies, differing by only a kilohertz or so and therefore received at one spot on the dial.

RTTY is generated by a typewriter-like machine or by computer. The receiving end prints the result on a similar typewriter-like printer or computer printer. The transmissions can best be described as a continuous "deedle-deedle-deedle" sound.

RTTY is used by news wire services, by the military, by embassies of the U.S. and foreign countries, by aeronautical services, by NOAA, and many other agencies and services.

To actually get a print out of received messages, you need additional equipment to connect to the audio output of your receiver. One option is to use older Teletype Corporation mechanical "page printers", available on the surplus market for under $200. A better option is to use a small computer and RTTY converter. The combination can be purchased for about $400 (see Figure 4-1). The computer approach has the advantage that many different types of RTTY formats can be received. Most RTTY transmissions are not encoded, but some use non-standard formats for privacy.

Figure 4-1.
RTTY Computer
Courtesy of Advanced Electronic Applications, Inc.

The number of RTTY stations is much too large to be included here—here's a sample of stations found in the short HF segment from 7.335 to 7.580:

7.335, 7.407, 7.430, 7.455, 7.477, 7.500, 7.580 MHz.

Single Sideband

Single sideband (SSB) is used as the major type of two-way communication with many users of the HF bands— military, commercial, aircraft, and amateur. Single sideband is a more efficient type of transmission—it delivers more energy to "punch through" the crowded HF bands.

As in the case of CW and RTTY, a receiver with a beat frequency oscillator (BFO) must be used to receive single sideband. Without a BFO, single sideband sounds much like Donald Duck, and this is the way that amateurs first referred to it (or as "Silly Sideband") before it became overwhelmingly popular.

A typical application for SSB is aircraft communication for long-distance flights. SSB on the HF bands is a good communication method for such flights because of the reliability of lower-frequency HF bands. A typical transmission observed while writing this book was two-way communication between an airlines dispatcher and a "heavy" (747, DC-10, or other jumbo jet) on 5.617 MHz during evening hours.

To tune in SSB stations, turn on the LSB or USB function. Turn down the RF gain to minimum and the AF gain or AUDIO to maximum. Now advance the RF gain for the signal involved as you tune across the dial. Switch to either upper or lower sideband by USB or LSB. IF the proper sideband is selected, you'll hear the signal become almost intelligible as the receiver is tuned across it. Rock the pitch control carefully until the signal becomes lifelike. The signal will *never* sound as clear as an AM signal, but it will be close. Once tuned in, you may have to "touch up" the pitch occasionally as the receiver drifts.

This same technique can often be used on AM signals that have adjacent channel interference to eliminate some of that interference. Chose either the upper or lower sideband to reduce interference from the adjacent signal. This works because of the selectivity of the SSB mode that allows only a single sideband to pass through the receiver's amplifier circuits.

Time and Frequency Signals

Among the other stations on the HF band are a number of time and frequency signals. These are stations that broadcast extremely accurate time signals on precisely known frequencies. The frequencies can be used as signal standards for calibrating radio equipment or other purposes.

The primary United States broadcaster of this type is the National Bureau of Standards station in Fort Collins, Colorado, WWV. WWV operates on 2.5, 5, 10, 15, and 20 MHZ with an accuracy of one part in 10 trillion!

(However, the path the radio wave takes to travel from the transmitter to your receiver via the ionosphere in one or more bounces will reduce the accuracy somewhat).

The time is announced by voice message every minute; clock ticks are sounded during most of the remaining time. In addition to the audio signals, specially encoded digital signals representing minutes, hours, and days are also sent on a 100-Hz "subcarrier".

In addition to WWV, the National Bureau of Standards operates WWVH in Kauai, Hawaii on 2.5, 5, 10, and 15 MHz, with the same accuracy as WWV, and WWVB on 60 kHz. WWVB does not have voice identification.

WWV on one of its frequencies can usually be heard anywhere in the United States as one of the strongest signals on the band. During periods of band inactivity due to the sunspot cycle, WWV often is one of the few readable stations.

Along with WWV/WWVH, another easy to find station is CHU, the time station of the National Research Council of Canada. It broadcasts time signals on 3.330, 7.335, and 14.670 MHz. A voice announcement of the time is made on each minute with clock ticks for every second.

There are a number of other international stations that also broadcast time and frequency signals. Many of these are on the same frequencies as WWV and WWVH, however, and are overridden by them. Station RID (USSR) is at 5.004, 10.004, and 15.004 MHz. Station VNG (Australia) is at 7.500 MHz.

Other foreign stations for time and frequency operate in the VLF and LF region, from 16 kHz to 185 kHz. One reason for stations operating on such low frequencies is that their signals are not much affected by propagation—they rely upon the ground wave for coverage.

During research on this book a spot check of all frequencies of WWV and CHU was made. All transmissions on all frequencies of both stations could be heard. Often WWVH can be heard in addition to WWV. WWVH appears (in the continental U.S.) as a background voice (female) after the WWV announcement.

Weather Maps by Facsimile

The U.S. Coast Guard, among others, transmits facsimile weather maps on the marine band (see above). These weather maps can be received and reproduced on facsimile systems on commercial vessels or even small boats. New technology makes the facsimile system cost affordable to the small boat owner. If you're thinking of taking that sail to the South Pacific on your 40-foot ketch, it might be a wise investment! Facsimile transmissions sound like a harsh buzzing—look for it in these bands.

Citizen's Band Frequencies

The Citizen's Band is on the top edge of the HF band. It was created out of the seldom-used 11-meter amateur band to provide a band for anyone who applied for a license. Knowledge of radio theory or code was not a prerequisite. Equipment used on the CB band consists of a 5-watt or less transmitter and integrated receiver (the entire unit is called a transceiver). There are 40 channels in the CB band, from 26.965 MHz up to 27.405 MHz.

Channel 23 (27.255 MHz) is used for radio control or garage door openers (although most users of radio control or garage door openers now operate in the UHF band to avoid interference). Channel 9 (27.065 MHz) is set aside for an emergency channel; it is normally open. Channel 19 (27.185 MHz) has historically been a "truckers" channel for reporting on traffic conditions and "smokies" (highway patrolmen). Channel 19 is an excellent one to monitor with a mobile CB rig, even though you may be hesitant to use it for two-way communication. It yields a great deal of information about highway safety conditions, a subject about which all professional drivers are concerned. (And if you hear talk about a smokie "taking pictures", consider slowing down to avoid the radar . . .)

The CB channels are listed in Table 4-1.

Table 4-1. Citizen's Band Frequencies

Channel #	Frequency	
1	26.965 MHz	(single owner)
2	26.975	'' ''
3	26.985	'' ''
4	27.005	'' ''
5	27.015	'' ''
6	27.025	'' . ''
7	27.035	'' ''
8	27.055	
9	27.065	(emergency)
10	27.075	
11	27.085	
12	27.105	
13	27.115	
14	27.125	
15	27.135	
16	27.155	(single owner)
17	27.165	'' ''
18	27.175	'' ''
19	27.185	'' ''
20	27.205	'' ''
21	27.215	'' ''
22	27.225	'' ''
23	27.255	

24	27.235
25	27.245
26	27.265
27	27.275
28	27.285
29	27.295
30	27.305
31	27.315
32	27.325
33	27.335
34	27.345
35	27.355
36	27.365
37	27.375
38	27.385
39	27.395
40	27.405

The Citizen's Band was intended for local communications. Communications with stations more than 150 miles distant is illegal, but widely done. The CB band is so crowded and there have been so many units sold, that it is virtually impossible to police the band.

The CB band can be received on any shortwave receiver that provides coverage of the CB frequencies. However, CB radios are so inexpensive that they offer the most convenient way to receive the CB frequencies. Another option is a *scanner* into which CB channels can be programmed (see Chapter 10).

The most common type of transmission on the Citizen's Band is AM, although some CBers use single sideband. SSB is growing in popularity because of crowded band conditions. The normal transmissions that can be heard are within a forty-mile radius, although this coverage can increase greatly during conditions in which the band is open—in this case it is possible to hear (and communicate with) stations thousands of miles away.

The Russian Woodpecker

A common form of interference on many bands is a signal that sounds like a car ignition—eight pulses per second in a rapid, annoying knocking appearing from one side of a frequency and going off the other side. Radio amateurs call this signal the "Russian Woodpecker", as it appears to be generated by an over-the-horizon defensive Russian radar installation. The Russian woodpecker was heard on the 25-meter band and others while researching this book. At times it can reappear repeatedly and be quite annoying.

Pirate and Clandestine Stations

Guerillas in South America, the Middle East, and other places around the world use radio communications on all frequencies. Although many of these are low-power transmissions, under the right conditions the signals can travel thousands of miles, or even around the world. In monitoring these transmissions, of course, it helps to speak fluent Spanish or Farsi!

Another type of clandestine radio broadcasting is transmission involving code groups. A voice (usually a female's) reads continuous strings of digits in five-letter groups. Typical transmissions observed recently, while preparing this book were on 6.768 MHz and 8.874 MHz in Spanish. Speculation among shortwave enthusiasts is that the code groups are instructions to agents of the United States and other powers.

Another type of unauthorized activity is *pirate radio stations*. For about $500, anyone can purchase a transceiver that can broadcast on virtually any frequency with a power output of several hundred watts. It appears that there will always be individuals that want to operate these pirate radio stations, playing music or expressing their own political or social views. The FCC, however, frowns on these activities and actively seeks out such pirate broadcasters to shut them down. Look for this activity on the short wavebands or the AM or FM broadcast bands. (Recently, even a major satellite broadcaster's telecast was preempted by a pirate!) Another source of pirate activity is near the CB bands, from CB operators using modified high-powered CB transmitters.

Another form of pirate station are high-powered transmitters located on ships. Radio Caroline, a ship-based station, operated offshore from Great Britain for several years, playing rock music. At the time only Government radio stations were allowed. Another recent North Sea pirate station was the MV Communicator, the ship from which Laser 558 radio broadcasts were made to Great Britain. The Communicator was recently towed into port by the British government after nearly sinking.

Chapter 5
Exploring VHF and UHF

VHF and UHF frequencies have an enormous amount of space available compared to the MF and HF bands. There is the same space available on the 3/4-meter amateur band (420 to 450 MHz) as in all available bands below 30 MHz, for example, and the 3/4-meter amateur band is just *one* small band in the VHF and UHF region!

Space in the VHF and UHF region is divided into *channels* for convenience in operating. Many of these channels are wider than they are in the MF and HF region because of the modulation techniques—frequency modulation (FM) requires more of a bandwidth than the AM or single-sideband used on the MF and HF bands. FM modulation is used almost exclusively for voice communication. Modes other than voice mode, such as television, take up a great deal more space. The minimum bandwidth for one channel of television, for example, is 5 MHz.

In this chapter we'll scan the VHF and UHF bands and show you what you can expect to find there. We'll progress from the 30 MHz lower limit to higher and higher frequencies.

30 - 49 MHz

Look for police operations here, especially State Police or Highway Patrol cars, which operate over a wider area than local law enforcement. Fire departments, ambulances and rescue squads, local government, common carriers (telephone services), trucking companies, and businesses will also be found.

The 49-MHz Citizen's Band

This band is used in FM mode for portable phones, the type that you can carry around with you. The handset frequency is in the 49.670—to 49.970-MHz range, while the base unit broadcasts in AM in the MF band—about 1.7 MHz— or in the VHF band—46.610—46.970 MHz. (Newer models have eliminated the HF band transmission.) Power for portable phones is not very great—in the fractions of a watt. Some users, however, have external antennas to extend the range for farm or range use. In these cases, you may be able to hear one or both ends of the conversation. In crowded metropolitan areas you may also be able to hear phone conversations. Respect the users privacy, as most callers are not aware that they can be overheard.

Portable phone frequencies are as follows:

49.670 MHz	46.610 MHz
49.770	46.710
49.830	46.770
49.845	46.630
49.860	46.670
49.875	46.730
49.890	46.830
49.930	46.870
49.970	46.970
49.990	46.930

Another use of this band is in hand-held *walkie-talkies*. This band is restricted to transmitters having less than 100 milliwatts of power, so the transmitting range will never be that great—possibly 1/2 mile—but occasionally you will hear children with inexpensive walkie talkies or perhaps an adult with a little more elaborate set. Line-of-sight communications, however, might be possible over tens of miles with a sensitive receiver.

Six-Meter Amateur Band, 50.0 to 54.0 MHz

This ham band used to be one of the highest frequency ham bands! Now, it has fallen out of favor as many hams have moved to two-meter and higher frequency operation. All amateur modes are used on six meters—CW, AM, SSB, FM, and RTTY. Reception with a scanner is possible, but only for FM stations. There are no rigid channels, although certain frequencies have been set aside for "calling" frequencies and beacons.

Communication over thousands of miles is possible on this band as it is intermediate in frequency between line-of-sight frequencies and the HF frequencies. Normal distances, however, are hundreds of miles or local.

VHF Television Channels 2 - 6, 54-88 MHz

The VHF television band occupies the frequencies from 54 through 80 MHz. Television audio is FM and can be received on a scanner or receiver covering those frequencies (but not very well because of the scanner's tighter bandwidth). The frequency assignments are shown below. Note that there is a gap between channels 4 and 5—4 MHz of space used for the 72 to 76-MHz CB band (see next paragraph):

Channel	Limits (MHz)		Video Carrier	Audio Carrier
2	54.00	60.00	55.25	59.75
3	60.00	66.00	61.25	65.75
4	66.00	72.00	67.25	71.75
5	76.00	82.00	77.25	81.75
6	82.00	88.00	83.25	87.75

The 72- to 76-MHz CB Band

This CB band is used for radio control purposes, but not for voice communication. It is sandwiched in between channels 4 and 5 of the low VHF television band.

FM Broadcast Band, 88-108 MHz

The United States FM broadcast band is found at 88.1 to 107.9 MHz. (In other parts of the world, this coverage is provided on 66-72 MHz (Eastern Europe) and 87-104 MHz.) Most scanners do not cover this band because there are so many FM radios that perform the task well. There are several scanners, however, that provide coverage of this band and others.

U.S. stations are assigned a channel 200 kHz wide. This allows for 108 -88 = 20 MHz or 200 channels on the band. There are several classes of transmitters, allowing up to 25 Kw (25,000 watts).

Transmissions are primarily line-of-sight with maximum distances about 120 miles. However, during certain times, longer transmissions are possible, and there are enthusiasts who try to receive DX FM broadcasts. A high yagi (normal TV type) antenna with rotator is good for this type of DXing.

Aircraft Band 108–135 MHz

This band is devoted to aircraft operations and navigation. Typically, you'll hear a commercial jet aircraft contact the Regional Air Traffic Control Center on one channel, for example, as the aircraft approaches Los Angeles over Las Vegas. As the aircraft then approaches Los Angeles Airport (LAX), the Regional Controller turns control over to the LAX Terminal Controller on a local channel, who controls the landing. After landing, the aircraft is turned over to the LAX Ground Control on yet another channel for taxiing. You may also hear the aircraft contacting their airline company on another channel. Other channels in this band are used by the Civil Air Patrol, helicopter operations, and almost any local communications relating to civilian aircraft.

One frequency used in the band, 121.5 MHz, is used as an EPIRB frequency, *Emergency Position Indicating Radiobeacon.* An EPIRB unit is a small device that broadcasts a distinctive tone and is used by pilots of downed aircraft or the crew of ships that have sunk. This frequency is monitored by commercial aircraft and satellites of several nations and used to home in for rescue. Another EPIRB frequency is 243.0 MHz.

OMNI stations are found in the band as well. OMNI stations are omnidirectional navigational transmitters—radiobeacons. They broadcast a continuous code, such as .../-..-/-.-. (SXC for Santa Catalina). Some also broadcast weather bulletins. OMNI stations are found all across the United States and Canada and have ranges from 30 to 200 miles or so for aircraft. Radiobeacons in the LF band (see Chapter 4) have been largely replaced by OMNI.

Weather Satellite Band, 136-138 MHz

NOAA, the national weather service, the USSR, and Japan all have working weather satellites that are continually transmitting weather maps that are free for the asking. Some of the satellites are in geosynchronous orbit—at the same point in the sky all the time. Others circle the earth in polar or other orbits. It is possible (see Figure 2-9) to receive the weather maps on equipment costing less than $500. The result can be high-quality photographs from space received in your own home. (A good reference book for this is "The New Weather Satellite Handbook"—see Appendix I.)

Satellite signals can be heard on 137.15 and 137.30 MHz (USSR METEOR satellite) and 137.50 and 137.62 MHz (NOAA TIROS satellites). Good reception requires an outside antenna with a circular polarization (combination vertical and horizontal polarization).

Two-Meter Amateur Band, 144-148 MHz

This is the most popular VHF or UHF amateur band. Like the six-meter band, a variety of types of transmission are allowed—everything from CW to FM. The greatest amount of activity, though, is in voice FM operation, which can be received on scanners or analog receivers.

Although the band is not divided up into exact channels, operation has evolved that way due to synthesized transceivers (transmitters and receivers). Most frequencies used are in 10-kHz increments (for example, 145.36 MHz).

The band is occupied in metropolitan areas by *repeaters*. Repeaters are stations on hills, mountaintops, or other favorable locations that rebroadcast signals they receive. A ham with a 3-watt HT (walkie-talkie) can call the repeater and have it rebroadcast his signal over a much wider area and with much greater power. Two-way or multiple conversations on *nets* can be easily accomplished on repeaters. Repeaters can be *open* to all hams or *closed*, limited in use to only members of a repeater group.

Occasionally you'll hear 1/2 second bursts of sound on two-meter channels that sound similar to HF RTTY transmissions. These are *packet radio* transmissions. Packet radio is a high-speed, error-checking type of RTTY used on VHF and UHF to send messages. There are now networks that allow these messages to be automatically sent hundreds of miles, and soon there will be packet satellite capability.

Marine Band, 156.050 - 157.425 MHz

This band is dedicated to local marine calling frequencies, including emergency channels. The band is used by commercial vessels in addition to weekend pleasure boaters. The transmission is FM and can easily be received by scanners having the proper frequency range. Marine frequencies are organized in channels, with a channel pair for base and ship—the base transmits on one frequency while the ship transmits on the other, in most cases.

The maximum output power for shipboard VHF sets is 25 watts. Ships obviously operate on sea level, so it's fairly easy to calculate the normal line-of-sight operating range of a marine VHF set. The distance in statute miles is

$$distance = 1.6 \times square \ root \ of \ (H)$$

where H is the height of the antenna in feet above the water. A small sailboat with an antenna 36 feet up on a mast can transmit about 9.6 miles, for example. Don't expect to receive too many shipboard transmissions, therefore, unless you happen to be near a boating area with a portable scanner! Of course, under the right conditions, you may hear shipboard transmissions several hundred miles away on VHF.

Channel 16 is a mandatory emergency channel, as is channel 6 (inter-ship communications). Channel 22 is used for communication with the Coast Guard. Other channels are used for ship-to-shore telephone (26, 28, 25, 27), bridge-to-bridge (13), and commercial use (9), among others.

Channel	Base	Ship	
1	160.050	156.050	
2	160.700	156.100	
3	160.750	156.150	
4	160.800	156.200	
5	160.850	156.250	
6	160.950	156.350	
7A	156.350	156.350	
8	156.400	156.400	
9	156.450	156.450	
10	156.500	156.500	
11	156.550	156.550	
12	156.600	156.600	
13	156.650	156.650	
14	156.700	156.700	
15	156.750	156.750	
16	156.800	156.800	
17	156.850	156.850	
18	161.500	156.900	
18A	156.900	156.900	
19	161.550	156.950	
20	161.600	157.000	
21	161.650	157.050	
21CG	157.050	157.050	Coast Guard
22	161.700	157.100	
22CG	157.100	157.100	Coast Guard

23	161.750	157.150	
23CG	157.150	157.150	Coast Guard
24	161.800	157.200	
25	161.850	157.250	
26	161.900	157.300	
27	161.950	157.350	
28	162.000	157.400	
60	160.875	156.275	
61	160.675	156.075	
62	160.725	156.125	
63	160.775	156.175	
64	160.825	156.225	
65	160.875	156.275	
65A	156.275	156.275	
66	160.925	156.325	
67	156.375	156.375	
68	156.425	156.425	
69	156.475	156.475	
70	156.525	156.525	
71	156.575	156.575	
72	156.625	156.625	
73	156.675	156.675	
74	156.725	156.725	
75			Coast Guard
76			Coast Guard
77	156.875	156.875	
78	161.525	156.925	
78A	156.925	156.925	
79	161.575	156.975	
80	161.625	157.075	
80A	157.025	157.025	
81	161.675	157.075	
82	161.725	157.125	
83	161.775	157.175	
83CG	157.175	157.175	Coast Guard
84	161.825	157.225	
85	161.875	157.275	
86	161.925	157.325	
87	161.975	157.375	
88	162.025	157.425	
88A	157.425	157.425	

NOAA Weather Stations, 162.4, 162.475, and 162.55 MHz

NOAA, the national weather service, operates more than 365 FM stations across the country that broadcast local and regional conditions. Weather is broadcast continually and includes temperatures, forecasts, agricultural information, and the like. Frequencies are either 162.400, 162.475, or 162.550 MHz. Transmissions can be received on any scanner, or any simple "weather radio". A steady 10-second tone indicates a following weather warning message and will activate weather receivers that can detect the tone (see Figure 5-1).

The Canadian weather channel is 161.650 MHz.

Figure 5-1.
Weather Radio
Courtesy of Radio Shack,
A Division of Tandy Corporation

Federal Agencies, 162-174 MHz

Many federal agencies use the frequencies in this part of the VHF spectrum, including U.S. Customs, the FCC, FBI, the National Park Service, and NASA. Another area used by federal agencies is in the region 406—420 MHz.

VHF Television Channels 7 through 13, 174-216 MHz

VHF channels 7 though 13 occupy frequencies from 174 MHz through

216 MHz. As with channels 2 through 6, the audio is FM and can be received on a scanner or other receiver, but not with good quality.

7	174.00	180.00	175.25	179.75
8	180.00	186.00	181.25	185.75
9	186.00	192.00	187.25	191.75
10	192.00	198.00	193.25	197.75
11	198.00	204.00	199.25	203.75
12	204.00	210.00	205.25	209.75
13	210.00	216.00	211.25	215.75

The 220 - to 225-MHz Ham Band

This is also a popular VHF amateur band. Like the two-meter band, a variety of types of transmissions are allowed—everything from CW to FM. Like the two-meter band, the greatest amount of activity is in voice FM operation, which can be received on scanners or analog receivers.

Although the band is not divided up into exact channels, operation has evolved that way due to synthesized transceivers (transmitters and receivers). Most frequencies used are in 10-kHz increments (for example, 223.98 MHz).

The one and a quarter-meter band also has its share of repeaters, second only to the two-meter band. Packet radio is also present, but not in the amounts there are on the two-meter band.

The 420 – to 450-MHz Ham Band

Amateurs are moving to this band because of overcrowding on the two-meter and 1 1/4-meter bands, at least in metropolitan areas. Like the other bands, various types of transmissions are allowed, including fast-scan amateur television. Again, any frequencies in the band can be used, but transceiver operation has created channels in multiples of 10 kHz. The wavelength of this band is 3/4 meters, and it is sometimes referred to in this fashion.

The 462-MHz CB Band

This CB band is shared with other services. Voice operation is permitted. Many garage door openers use this frequency. The frequency range is 462.525 through 467.475 MHz.

UHF Television Channels 14 through 83, 470-890 MHz

UHF channels 14 though 83 occupy frequencies from 470 MHz through 890 MHz. As with channels 2 through 13, the audio is FM and can be received on a scanner or other receiver, but not with good quality.

Channel	Limits (MHz)		Video Carrier	Audio Carrier
14	470.00	476.00	471.25	475.75
15	476.00	482.00	477.25	481.75
16	482.00	488.00	483.25	487.75
17	488.00	494.00	489.25	493.75
18	494.00	500.00	495.25	499.75
19	500.00	506.00	501.25	505.75
20	506.00	512.00	507.25	511.75
21	512.00	518.00	513.25	517.75
22	518.00	524.00	519.25	523.75
23	524.00	530.00	525.25	529.75
24	530.00	536.00	531.25	535.75
25	536.00	542.00	537.25	541.75
26	542.00	548.00	543.25	547.75
27	548.00	554.00	549.25	553.75
28	554.00	560.00	555.25	559.75
29	560.00	566.00	561.25	565.75
30	566.00	572.00	567.25	571.75
31	572.00	578.00	573.25	577.75
32	578.00	584.00	579.25	583.75
33	584.00	590.00	585.25	589.75
34	590.00	596.00	591.25	595.75
35	596.00	602.00	597.25	601.75
36	602.00	608.00	603.25	607.75
37	608.00	614.00	609.25	613.75
38	614.00	620.00	615.25	619.75
39	620.00	626.00	621.25	625.75
40	626.00	632.00	627.25	631.75
41	632.00	638.00	633.25	637.75
42	638.00	644.00	639.25	643.75
43	644.00	650.00	645.25	649.75
44	650.00	656.00	651.25	655.75
45	656.00	662.00	657.25	661.75
46	662.00	668.00	663.25	667.75
47	668.00	674.00	669.25	673.75
48	674.00	680.00	675.25	679.75
49	680.00	686.00	681.25	685.75
50	686.00	692.00	687.25	691.75
51	692.00	698.00	693.25	697.75
52	698.00	704.00	699.25	703.75
53	704.00	710.00	705.25	709.75
54	710.00	716.00	711.25	715.75

55	716.00	722.00	717.25	721.75
56	722.00	728.00	723.25	727.75
57	728.00	734.00	729.25	733.75
58	734.00	740.00	735.25	739.75
59	740.00	746.00	741.25	745.75
60	746.00	752.00	747.25	751.75
61	752.00	758.00	753.25	757.75
62	758.00	764.00	759.25	763.75
63	764.00	770.00	765.25	769.75
64	770.00	776.00	771.25	775.75
65	776.00	782.00	777.25	781.75
66	782.00	788.00	783.25	787.75
67	788.00	794.00	789.25	793.75
68	794.00	800.00	795.25	799.75
69	800.00	806.00	801.25	805.75
70	806.00	812.00	807.25	811.75
71	812.00	818.00	813.25	817.75
72	818.00	824.00	819.25	823.75
73	824.00	830.00	825.25	829.75
74	830.00	836.00	831.25	835.75
75	836.00	842.00	837.25	841.75
76	842.00	848.00	843.25	847.75
77	848.00	854.00	849.25	853.75
78	854.00	860.00	855.25	859.75
79	860.00	866.00	861.25	865.75
80	866.00	872.00	867.25	871.75
81	872.00	878.00	873.25	877.75
82	878.00	884.00	879.25	883.75
83	884.00	890.00	885.25	889.75

How to Find Additional VHF and UHF Stations

One of the problems with using scanners is that the VHF and UHF bands are just too big! It would be impossible to list all users in the VHF and UHF region, simply because there are too many. The Fox Marketing, Inc. "Fox Scanner Radio Listings", for example, lists all scanner stations in the Los Angeles area and has 392 pages of 64-line listings! Equivalent listings are available for other metropolitan areas and are just as large. Included in the listings are such diverse stations as:

- Police
- Fire
- Ambulance
- Hospitals
- Emergency Medical

- Trucking
- Mobile Telephone
- Cellular Telephone
- Business Repeaters
- Local Government

Another book, "Government Radio Systems" (Mobile Radio Sources, 1984) provides 136 pages of city, county, state, and federal government stations in California alone.

To find interesting channels in your area:

- Find a book of local listings, usually available at scanner dealers or electronics shops.
- Talk to your local Radio Shack store. Since they are actively selling scanners, they always know the interesting local channels.
- Scan the channels yourself, compiling a list as you find new stations.

Compiling a list of channels would be easy if the stations were on the air continuously. However, most stations (except for taxi dispatchers and the like) operate in brief bursts. You'll find that it's relatively easy to find the dispatchers, mobile telephone operating frequencies, and other frequent users, but there are many that may only broadcast a few times an hour. But then again, that's what makes operating a scanner so interesting. There's always the new station to be found and added to the list of exciting communications.

Chapter 6.
Amateur Radio

No one knows why radio amateurs are called "hams"—perhaps they hammed it up in the early days of broadcasting. However, the name has stuck. Any time you hear the name "ham" it will refer to a radio amateur, and we'll use it here. Just what is a ham? Does it take a radio genius?

Hams come from every walk of life (see Figure 6-1). You're liable to make contact with a postman, an electronics engineer, a housewife, or an astronaut. There are about 450,00 hams in the United States and many more world-wide, in virtually all countries.

What it Takes to Become A Radio Amateur

Every ham must be licensed by the Federal Communications Commission. There are various classes of licenses, with more privileges accorded to the higher classes of licenses. To get a license you must take an examination concerning operating rules and standards and radio fundamentals. You must also pass a code test. The classes of licenses and exam requirements are as follows:

- Novice Class—This allows you to operate in selected bands with limited power in CW (code), voice (SSB), and RTTY. The exam covers fundamentals and operating procedures. The code test is for code received at five words per minute.
- Technician Class—This license is geared to VHF and UHF voice communications in addition to novice class privileges. The exam covers the Novice class material and additional theory. The code test is for five words per minute.
- General Class—The majority of hams hold this class of license. Almost all privileges are allowed an all bands. Exceptions are small segments of certain bands. The exam covers the Novice and Technician class material. The code test is for 13 words per minute.
- Advanced Class—This is the second highest license and allows a few additional ranges of frequencies to be used. The exam covers the General class material and additional theory. The code test is for 13 words per minute.
- Extra Class—This is the highest license and offers all amateur privileges. The exam covers the Advanced material and additional theory. The code test is for 20 words per minute.

The licenses are not consecutive—you could, for example, take the Extra class license test and receive an immediate Extra class license without having had any lower licenses or amateur experience.

How tough are the exams? The Novice Exam consists of 30 questions out of a list of 110. The General class exam consists of 50 questions out of 500. The key here is that the questions are all *published* and a random sampling then makes up the test. Obviously, the first thought that comes to mind is that one could memorize the answers to all of the questions (even 500) and pass the test more easily. In fact, many do this. However, others take a radio theory test and have a thorough background in the material.

The code test at five words per minute is not really that difficult. Five words per minute is about one character every two seconds, so you have a chance to search your memory and then write down the correct character. At 13 words a minute, the code comes at you almost three times as fast, but it is still possible to achieve this speed in a matter of a few dozen hours. The Extra Class code test at 20 words per minute requires more practical experience in copying code; most people cannot come up to this rate of code speed without having practical experience.

There has been growing pressure in recent years to reduce or eliminate the code requirements, and to make the written exam easier. The latter has already happened as a practical matter; questions were never published as they are now. Old timers grumble about "appliance operators" without a technical background and new licensees talk about how useless code is. In spite of cynics, however, the people in the hobby maintain a fairly high level of technical competence. They are among the most knowledgeable and inquisitive hobbyists of all.

The ARRL and Ham Radio Clubs

One of the best known representatives of hams is the American Radio Relay League in Newington, CT. The ARRL has been representing hams since the inception of the hobby. They have a de facto lobbying power in representing ham radio. Since the radio spectrum *is* crowded, there is a continual fight for frequency bands among commercial users, the government, and hams. Most would say the ARRL does a good job in preserving the amateur frequencies.

In addition to lobbying for hams, the ARRL operates an organization station, W1AW. This station transmits ham bulletins, ham news, and code practice on many ham bands and can be heard around the United States at regular times.

For information on ARRL activities, contact

The American Radio Relay League
Newington, CT 06111

Loosely affiliated with the ARRL, or in some cases, not affiliated at all, are hundreds of ham radio clubs across the country. These clubs hold free classes for code and theory exams, social meetings, and "hamfests"— conventions of hams on a regional or national level.

It's safe to say that if you are interested in amateur radio, virtually any ham or club will be more than happy to talk to you about it, tell you how to proceed, and fill you in on local amateur happenings.

What Are Your Responsibilities As a Ham?

Hams have to pay their keep, the radio spectrum being as crowded as it is. They did this initially by being a source of well-trained operators for wartime conditions and for emergency communications. Although the former goal is perhaps not as valid as it once was, in these days of automated and sophisticated military communications, the latter still applies.

Hams continually provide well organized and efficient communications in all types of emergencies, ranging from blizzards to earthquakes. In the 1985 Mexico City earthquake, for example, hams were instrumental in coordinating rescue operations, reporting on local conditions, and finding missing family members. Hams across the United States and other countries in addition to those in Mexico City were involved. The very nature of ham radio—widespread local stations that are immediately usable with well-trained operators and state-of-the-art equipment—make ham radio a bargain.

Hams cannot use their hobby as a tool in business—they must not charge for their services. In addition to emergency communications, hams provide such services as "phone patches"—worldwide links between servicemen and their families—and communications at community events.

Lest you think that ham radio is all work and no play, however, it's safe to say that there are many hams that are in the hobby purely for the enjoyment it offers them. And there are plenty of activities in ham radio.

The Enjoyment of Ham Radio

CW stands for "continuous wave" and means code operation. (The transmitter is keyed on and off without any voice modulation, hence the wave is continuous.) There are many hams that are code buffs, especially since none of the MF and HF ham bands allow novice voice communication. Code has always had a following, but small computers in ham radio have made CW even easier. Messages can now be entered via the computers's keyboard—the computer takes over the task of converting the text character to code characters. On the receiving end, the computer also decodes the characters, displaying the message on the computer screen. There are even dedicated computers designed specifically for ham radio applications.

Coupled with automatic generation of CW characters is computer radio teleprinter (RTTY) operation. It's still possible to buy and use antiquated Teletype Corporation teleprinters, about the size of large typewriters. However, the trend these days is definitely towards computers with software that connects to the amateur transceiver and automatically transmits radio teleprinter characters. The computer program also translates incoming characters and displays the results on the screen. For MF and HF bands, operation at rates up to 30 characters per second (300 baud) is possible. On VHF and higher bands, the FCC allows 120 characters per second (1200 baud) and greater.

The ultimate RTTY is called "packet switching". Packet switching is primarily used on VHF or UHF amateur bands to send packets of data at 1200 baud rates or more. The data is like radio teleprinter data, but contains a great deal of error checking logic so that the messages can be sent virtually error free by retransmission of small segments of the message if necessary. More than one station can use the same channel, by interleaving packets (see Figure 6-2). By using VHF or UHF repeaters, called *digipeaters*, packet messages can be routed for hundreds or even thousands of miles. Coupled with satellite communications, packet switching messages can be routed around the world.

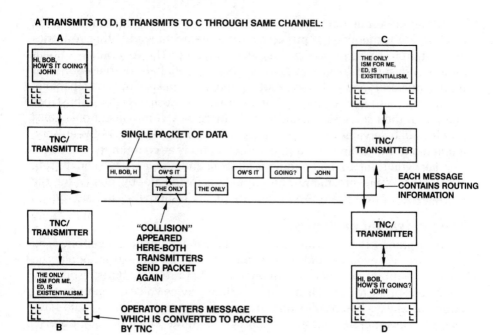

Figure 6-2.
Packet Switching Operation

A version of radio teleprinting called AMTOR is also popular on MF and HF bands. AMTOR is an adaptation of SITOR, a marine communications scheme. Like packet switching, it allows for retransmission of message segments to permit almost error-free messages.

Satellite communication is possible for every ham. The ARRL OSCAR satellites allow hams to transmit on an uplink frequency, which is then repeated on a downlink frequency by the satellite. Since the satellite views a large portion of the earth, VHF and UHF line-of-sight communications can be expanded over half the globe.

Satellites are *active* reflectors—they retransmit the signal. Even before hams used satellite communications, they established the moon as a passive reflector to echo signals back to earth! Hams have been using this form of communication since 1960. It takes a powerful transmitter and some technical expertise, but it's done on a fairly regular basis.

You may have seen newspaper headlines recently about the military using meteor trails as a means of VHF or UHF communication. This idea was developed by ham radio VHF experimentation. A meteor ionizes a high-altitude trail which lasts long enough for bursts of communication.

In addition to these technical pursuits, there is a great deal of activity in slow-scan television on the MF and HF ham bands. Pictures can be transmitted in about eight seconds and are made up of 120 lines, with each line a continuous scan. Even color pictures are currently being transmitted by a variety of techniques, including encoding in computer format.

Eschewing high technology, some hams just love to "rag-chew", speaking to other *net* members on a regular basis. There are hundreds of national nets, ranging from nets covering computers to chess nets and even to a net made up of Sherlock Holmes fans!

DXers are hams who contact foreign countries. One goal is to become a "DX Century Club" member by having talked to 100 countries or more. The current record for foreign contacts is over 360 countries. New countries are so much in demand that hams organize "DXpeditions" to set up temporary stations on islands or small countries that have little or no ham activity.

Contests are another element of ham activity. One of the most popular contests is "Field Day" in which points are awarded not only for many contacts, but for portable or mobile operation. Another popular contest is "Sweepstakes" in which hams make as many contacts as possible. The activity heard during such a contest is overwhelming. There is seemingly not a spot in the band that does not have a station transmitting for the contest!

Ham Bands

Ham Bands have evolved and changed over the years. For a long period, hams had use of the 80-meter, 75-meter, 40-meter, 20-meter, 15-meter, 11-meter, and 10-meter MF and HF bands, corresponding roughly to the 3.5-MHz, 4-MHz, 7-MHz, 14-MHz, 21-MHz, 28-MHz, and 30-MHz frequency bands. Not too many years ago, the 11-meter band was converted to Citizen's Band use. Recently, the 30- and 12-meter bands (about 10 and 25 MHz) were turned over to ham use. The MF and HF ham bands now stand as follows:

Band (Meters)	Frequency Range (MHz)
160	1.8 - 2.0
80, 75	3.5 - 4.0
40	7.0 - 7.3
30	10.1 - 10.15
20	14.0 - 14.35
15	21.0 - 21.45
12	24.89 - 24.99
10	28.0 - 29.7

The ham bands above 10 meters have also evolved. Not too many years ago, these bands were not used at all, due to the limitations of the electronic hardware available. Wartime (World War II) development spurred the use of radar and high-frequency devices, and eventual use of these bands. As they now stand, VHF and above ham bands are:

Band (Meters)	Frequency Range (MHz)
6	50.0 - 54.0
2	144.0 - 148.0
1 1/4	220 - 225
3/4	420 - 450
	902 - 928
	1240 - 1300
	2300 - 2450
	3300 - 3500
	5650 - 5925

Frequency Range (GHz)
10.0 - 10.5
24.0 - 24.25
48 - 50
71 - 76
165 - 170
240 - 250
300 and above

Tuning in the Ham Bands

To tune in the MF and HF ham bands, you'll need a shortwave receiver or general coverage receiver with a beat frequency oscillator or BFO. An occasional station will be found in the 160-to 10-meter ham bands that still uses AM transmission, but these are few and far between. It isn't that AM transmission isn't allowed, it's just that single-sideband (SSB) transmission is extremely popular and more efficient.

Without a BFO on a receiver, CW transmissions will either not be heard or will sound like a hissing and SSB transmissions will sound garbled. The BFO is a oscillator that is almost the same frequency as the received signal. The difference between the BFO and received signal produces a tone in the audio range and CW will now sound like a code practice oscillator tone.

Tuning in CW transmissions is easy with a BFO. Tuning in SSB signals is a little more involved. The BFO in this case replaces the missing carrier frequency, which has been removed before transmission. The carrier frequency inserted must be exactly equal to the missing carrier frequency. For this reason, a stable BFO frequency is called for—one that doesn't change much with heat or vibration. The SSB station is tuned in by slowly tuning past one side of the signal until a reasonable voice is heard, and then slightly rocking the tuning control until the voice sounds as nearly normal as possible. The best case voice will be almost as good as AM; however, some would say that SSB voices never sound normal.

Tuning in radio teleprinter, slow-scan television, and AMTOR on the MF and HF ham bands also requires a BFO.

On the VHF and UHF bands, however, ham band stations can be tuned in without a BFO since most transmissions are FM. Scanners receive only FM as all services in the VHF and UHF bands transmit with FM and amateur stations are no exception. To tune in ham stations, simply set your scanner for continuous scanning in the frequencies listed above. You'll soon find out the active channels and repeater frequencies in your area.

Chapter 9 describes amateur radio equipment and tells you what to look for if you're interested in "reading the mail" (simply listening) or possibly buying a transceiver that can be used for reception immediately and for transmitting after you get your license.

Section II
Radio Equipment

Chapter 7.
Shortwave Receivers

In this chapter we'll look at some of the currently available shortwave receiving equipment. There is quite a price variation in this equipment. Receivers at the high end are $500 or more and receivers at the low end are priced at about $50. Just about any receiver will easily receive Radio Moscow and the BBC World Service. What then do you get for the extra cost? To a large extent you are buying a digital tuning and readout capability with *programmability* in the more expensive receivers. Other factors are better performance as far as sensitivity and selectivity. We'll discuss these factors and others here.

Band Coverage
Basic Shortwave Receiver

There is a wide variation in the bands covered among shortwave receivers. A typical shortwave receiver (see Figure 7-1) will provide coverage of these bands by a selector switch:

- 150 - 260 kHz (long wave)
- 550 - 1500 kHz (AM broadcast band)
- 4.5 -5.5 MHz (shortwave)
- 5.9 -7.5 MHz (shortwave)
- 8.2 -10 MHz (shortwave)
- 11.4 - 14 MHz (shortwave)
- 14.6 - 18.2 MHz (shortwave)
- 21 - 25 MHz (shortwave)
- 98 - 108 MHz (FM broadcast band)

There are segments in these frequency slices that are not used by shortwave broadcasters—the shortwave portion of the 8.2—to 10-MHz slice, for example, is only in 9.5—to 9.9-MHz. However, it's better to have too much coverage than too little. The addition of the AM and FM broadcast bands means that you have a portable, battery-powered radio that provides not only local coverage, but allows you to listen to the world no matter where you are!

A typical radio of this type does not provide the capability to receive CW, radio teleprinter, or single-sideband transmissions, as it has no beat frequency oscillator (see below). However, if your interest is in receiving voice transmissions of foreign broadcasters, a low-cost receiver of this type will do very well.

Figure 7-1.
Basic Shortwave Receiver
Courtesy of Radio Shack,
A Division of Tandy Corporation

Continuous Coverage Analog Receivers

The next category of receiver is one that provides continuous coverage of all frequencies from the low end of the AM broadcast band (550 kHz) to 30 MHz. Often, this is a *communications receiver* incorporating the ability to receive CW, radio teleprinter, and single sideband. The frequency coverage is liable to be broken up into five or six bands, each covering progressively larger chunks of the overall frequency range. In this type of tuning, different coils are manually switched to select the general band (4.5 to 12 MHz, for example). After the band has been selected, a capacitor or other electronic part is rotated to change the received frequency within the band. A readout dial with a pointer or log scale is linked mechanically to the capacitor to provide the frequency at which a signal is being received.

This type of receiver has the advantage of providing coverage of any frequency. Even if your primary interest is in shortwave broadcasts, you may want to occasionally listen in on ham radio communications or commercial stations.

Ten to 30 years ago, there were a variety of companies making general coverage communications receivers and amateur equipment—such companies as Hallicrafters, Hammerlund, Collins, National Radio, Drake and others. These companies no longer manufacture this equipment because of competition from Japan, a country with an extremely active shortwave and amateur population and fine products as well.

Older communications receivers and amateur equipment, however, is available, and most of it will give excellent results. This equipment will not have the digital readouts described below—it will have a slide rule dial with manual band selection and tuning. In some cases it will be bulky— typically receivers of 30 years ago, for example, were 16 inches wide by eight inches high by 16 inches deep to accommodate large power supplies for the vacuum tubes used. However, if you can put up with these inconveniences, older receivers for the HF bands will provide a great deal of listening pleasure. Look for them at local ham radio clubs and swap meets.

Continuous Coverage Digital Receivers

More expensive receivers (see Figure 7-2) *synthesize* the frequencies used in receiving signals. Unlike analog receivers, not all frequencies can be selected in a band. Frequencies are selected rather in discrete steps of 10 or 100 Hz. Using this type of tuning, one could never receive 9,887,876 Hz—the closest you could come would be 9,887,900 Hz. However, this is close enough—a signal 100 hertz away for all intents and purposes is the same as one 0.0 hertz away, as the *passband* of the receiver transmits both at very close to the same signal level.

The frequency selected is usually displayed on an *LCD* (liquid crystal display). Sometimes an *LED* (red light emitting diode) display is used, but LCD displays use little power and lend themselves to battery-powered

Figure 7-2.
Digital Receiver
Courtesy Yaesu Electronics Corp.

portable applications. The LCD display is the same type of display you'll find on digital clocks or watches. Instead of seeing a movable pointer on a dial that represents the selected frequency, you'll see a digital readout with the frequency digits.

Synthesized receivers with digital tuning lend themselves to all kinds of tuning tricks. Scanning can be done by changing the frequency an increment at a time. This amounts to a new "channel" every 100 cycles. A scan on the 31-meter band would display 9.500.0 (9,500,000 Hz), then 9.500.1 (9,500,100 Hz), then 9.500.2 (9,500,200 Hz), and so forth. Given the proper electronics, specific frequencies can be entered with a few control panel buttons for scanning of a set of frequencies. You might scan between 9.5 MHz and 9.75 MHz and then between 15.1 and 15.45 MHz, for example. You could also enter widely different frequencies on different bands and with the flick of a button, rapidly switch between them. With some receivers you could also *interface* them to a small computer system for automatic selection of frequencies or bands (one acquaintance of the author uses a general coverage digital receiver linked to a computer to automatically scan and log teleprinter transmissions). One scheme for doing this is a built-in RS-232-C interface that allows all front panel control functions to be controlled by an interfacing computer with the proper software.

The trend among shortwave and general coverage receivers is definitely toward synthesized receivers, whether the receiver is a hand-held portable, or a larger fixed station model.

Beat Frequency Oscillator (BFO)

A receiver uses a beat frequency oscillator (BFO) to tune in CW, SSB, radio teleprinter, and other types of interesting transmissions. If a receiver does not have a BFO, it can only be used for AM voice transmissions, which encompass all of the usual foreign broadcasts. Still, given a choice between a receiver *with* a BFO and one without, it would probably be wiser to choose the one with the BFO so that you can receive the occasional commercial single-sideband or amateur station.

Selectivity

Selectivity is the ability of a receiver to reject unwanted signals while allowing a selected station to come through. Selectivity is important in the crowded radio spectrum. In receivers with poor selectivity, adjacent signals will sound nearly as loud as the signal to which you are tuned, or a more powerful adjacent signal will overpower the weaker signal you are trying to hear, as shown in Figure 7-3.

Unfortunately, good selectivity and good audio fidelity are at cross purposes. An FM broadcast band station can provide a frequency response of 50 to 15 kHz. The 15kHz frequencies transmitted are at the hearing limit of many listeners. The *bandwidth* of a typical shortwave station, however, is

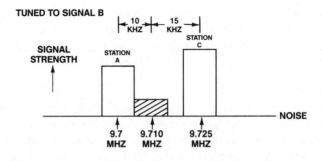

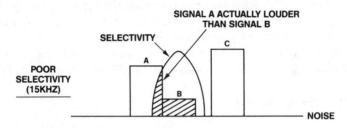

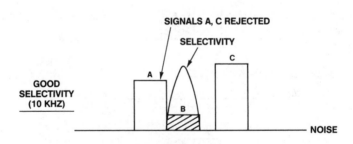

Figure 7-3.
Selectivity in a Shortwave
Receiver

much less than this. Good shortwave or communications receivers allow about 5.5-kHz selectivity to eliminate the usual continual interference from adjacent stations. Many receivers also allow additional selectivity to be switched in, allowing a frequency response up to 2.5 kHz under conditions where there is interference. Even the 5.5-kHz selectivity does not allow a very wide frequency range for reception of music. It is more than adequate for voice broadcasting, however.

For CW reception, the selectivity can be adjusted to 500 Hz or even less on the high-end receivers. CW reception doesn't require that a *band* of frequencies is passed, but only that a single frequency is passed. *Crystal filters,* fairly expensive selective devices, are used to change the selectivity.

Some receivers not only have good selectivity, but enhance the rejection of unwanted signals by *filtering*. In filtering, an interfering signal is rejected by a filter that sharply rejects a specific frequency (a "notch") filter or enhances the signal being received (see Figure 7-4).

Sensitivity

Sensitivity is usually not a problem with modern receivers. Sensitivity refers to the ability to receive weak signals and is measured by the minimum signal present at the antenna terminals to produce a readable output with a (usually) 10-db *signal-to-noise* ratio. A 10-db signal-to-noise ratio means that the audio signal is 10 decibels over the noise heard with no signal. One decibel is the minimum detectable increase in audio level. Ten decibels would be approximately the difference between a quiet whisper and an average whisper. Typical good sensitivity figures would be less than 4 microvolts for a 10-db signal-to-noise ratio for AM reception on the HF band.

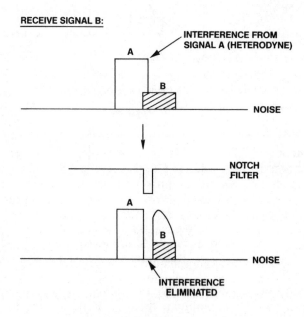

Figure 7-4.
Filtering in a Receiver

Variable Modes

More expensive receivers will have a variable mode control, allowing you to select either CW, AM, LSB, or USB. AM, of course, is most often used for shortwave broadcasting. The CW mode turns on the beat frequency oscillator of the receiver and enables code or radio teleprinter reception.

The LSB and USB modes are necessary for reception of single-sideband (SSB) signals. SSB is widely used on amateur radio transmissions and for commercial services and the military as well. The selection of either LSB or USB determines which *sideband* is used in reception of a single-sideband signal. AM transmission has a carrier and two sidebands that echo the 3-kHz frequencies required for recognizable voice communication, making the bandwidth of the AM signal about 6-kHz wide. In SSB, the carrier and one of the sidebands is filtered out, leaving the SSB signal only about 3-kHz wide. Which sideband remains, upper or lower, affects tuning and selectivity of the received signal. If the wrong sideband is selected for receiving, it will be rejected and the signal will almost disappear due to the receiver's selectivity.

Almost all receivers that allow CW and SSB reception will also have an *RF gain* control. This control is used in conjunction with the *audio gain* when receiving CW or SSB. It's a necessity to prevent overloading the receiver's radio-frequency circuits in these modes.

Other Receiver Features

Stability of receivers is not as important in shortwave receivers as in receivers for amateur purposes, unless CW or SSB is being received. A stable receiver doesn't change frequency at the slightest vibration. It also doesn't change frequency much as it heats up. Receivers with poor stability will have to be continually retuned on SSB signals to make the audio intelligible. A good receiver might need "touching up" only after ten minutes or greater.

Antenna tuners allow a wide range of antennas to be connected to the receiver. Receivers without antenna tuners are usually limited to a *50- or 75-ohm* antenna input, the characteristic *impedance* (see antenna section) of a half-wave dipole antenna and other common types. Not having an antenna tuner doesn't mean you won't be able to receive stations, it just means that the antenna you are connecting to may not be transferring the signal it receives without power loss. Often, you'll be able to operate the receiver with a built in telescoping antenna without any external antenna, but see Chapter 11 for hints on how an antenna will improve reception.

Most amateur receivers have more than enough *audio amplification.* Three watts of audio power, for example, is not a comfortable listening level for most people. A headphone jack and internal speaker are usually provided. You may want to use external speakers (provided with matching cases for the more expensive receivers) or connect to an external amplifier or tape recorder for logging reception. Some receivers will provide a recorder output.

A *squelch* control enables the audio of the receiver only when a signal is present. Without the squelch, you'll hear the continual hiss and crash of background noise, a real problem on MF and HF bands. With the squelch, you'll hear nothing unless there is a station strong enough to "override the squelch". The squelch level is settable to strong or weak signals. However, squelch is not as useful on the HF bands as it is in the VHF and UHF bands where the signal level is more constant.

S-meters in receivers show the strength of the received signal. They are not a necessity, but a convenient feature to have. Some receivers also show a SINPO signal graph along with the signal level readings (see Chaper 3).

Digital *clock displays* are available in the newer receivers. They are a convenient feature when listening to shortwave broadcasts and trying to receive station id.

Converters

A *converter* is an electronic circuit that converts one frequency range into another frequency range that can be received on existing equipment. You can, for example, buy converters that change the CB band into signals that can be received by a normal AM car radio, as shown in Figure 7-5. A CB signal on channel 1 at 26.965 MHz is *mixed* with a local oscillator frequency of 26 MHz. The result is a sum and difference frequency of 0.965 MHz and 52.965 MHz. The 52.965 MHz result is discarded, leaving a 0.965 MHz signal that is received at the 0.965 MHz spot on the AM dial by the car radio. A CB signal on channel 40 at 27.405 is received at 1.405 MHz. Intermediate CB channels are received between 0.964 and 1.405.

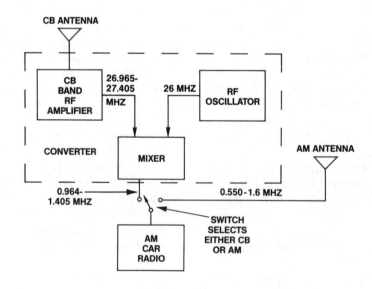

Figure 7-5.
Typical Converter Operation

The same principle can be applied to any band of frequencies, *down converting* them to lower frequencies or *up converting* them to higher frequencies. Some transceivers or receivers, for example, have optional converters for receiving UHF or VHF. The signal is then applied to the receiver input and read as a signal in the receiver's normal tuning range.

Converters may cost from $50 to $200 or more, and are somewhat of a compromise in ease of operation when compared to a receiver that allows extended frequency coverage, especially since receiver prices are not all that great when compared to the converter price. It may also be a convenience to have more than one receiver—one that handles the HF bands, and one that handles VHF and UHF.

Other Receiving Equipment

In addition to the options found *on* receivers, there are a number of other items that make using a receiver more pleasant. Some of them are discussed below.

A good *tape recorder* is a convenience for recording shortwave transmissions. Since many of the transmissions you hear may not be very clear, expecially for DX work, it pays to use the highest fidelity recorder possible. Cassette tape recorders rather than reel-to-reel are good, as reception can be easily stored as individual records and more easily filed.

Headphones are almost a necessity if you're listening in noisy environments, as many households are due to dishwashers, vacuums, and offspring. They also save wear and tear on other household members during late-evening listening sessions. The headphones you're looking for are *not* the stereo headphones used on audio equipment, but *monaural* headphones, sometimes called a *monophonic headset.* However, stereo headphones can be converted to monaural headphones quite easily by a stereo-to-mono headphone adapter (see Figure 7-6). Adapters are available to convert to a 1/4-inch or 1/8-inch mono plug.

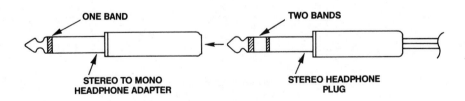

ONE BAND   TWO BANDS

STEREO TO MONO   STEREO HEADPHONE
HEADPHONE ADAPTER   PLUG

Figure 7-6.
Stereo to Monaural Headphone
Adapter

World maps are a convenience in locating countries or states, in measuring distances, and in finding time zone differences. Bear in mind, though, that most maps will not give a true *heading* for orientating antennas. Use a globe to find true headings.

Power supplies may be necessary for some equipment, such as radios that are designed to be powered from automobile 12-volt battery power. Power supplies that supply 12 volts dc from 110-volt household voltage are available from Radio Shack for under $50.

Frequency calibrators are electronic devices that generate a standard frequency signal such as 100 kHz. This signal can be compared to WWV/WWVH and then adjusted to give a precise frequency of 100 kHz. The device will then provide a set of signals that are spaced 100 kHz apart and can be used to calibrate the receiver's tuning dial (for analog receivers).

Chapter 8.
Citizen's Band
(CB) Equipment

In this chapter we'll look at some of the currently available Citizen's Band equipment. This equipment is intended for the 11-meter Citizen's Band. There are other "citizens bands", such as the 462.525—to 467.475-MHz band, but none has achieved the success of the 11-meter band, both in available equipment and user interest. The equipment we'll discuss in this chapter will be equipment designed for the 11-meter band.

A VolksRadio

All CB equipment for this band contains both a transmitter and receiver section and is very simple to operate. There is no involved transmitter or receiver tuning as there is in the case of some amateur equipment or even some shortwave receivers. The whole philosophy behind CB radio is that it should be a service that the general public can easily use for local communications. Because the units are low power (input power of five watts or less) the units are physically compact and easy to mount in cars or trucks. The 11-meter band also lends itself to small antennas—a one-quarter wave whip antenna is about 108 inches, or half that size when a *loading coil* is used.

CB *transceivers,* as a combined transmitter and receiver are called, are characterized by the following features.

Frequency Coverage

All CB transceivers cover the entire CB band, which consists of 40 channels, numbered 1 through 40. Each channel is 10-kHz wide, which is more than adequate for AM or SSB broadcasting. Most transceivers are only of the AM type, but some also have a single-sideband capability.

As a CB operator, you don't actually have to know the channel frequencies. They are listed in Chapter 4 for reference only. No other channels except those listed can be used for transmission.

Operating Controls

CB rigs are simplicity themselves. The simplest CB transceiver (see Figure 8-1) has only three controls:

- A channel select selects a channel from 1 through 40. The channel number appears in an LED display as the channel is selected.
- A volume control controls the volume of the received signal, as on any radio.
- A *squelch* control turns on the receiver sound only when a signal is

present over the background noise. The squelch level can be adjusted so that weaker or stronger signals turn on the audio. It is usually adjusted just beyond the point at which the background noise last triggers the audio on. Even a weak input signal then "breaks the squelch".

Figure 8-1.
Simple CB Transceiver
Courtesy of Radio Shack,
A Division of Tandy Corporation

To transmit with such a set, you'd turn the channel selector to the proper channel (avoid channel 9, an emergency channel only), listen to see that no one else was already transmitting on the channel, adjust the squelch, and then hold down the button on the microphone while speaking into it. After transmitting, you'd release the microphone button and listen to see if anyone replied.

More sophisticated CB sets have a few more knobs and buttons. There may be a switch marked "ANL" OFF and ON. The ANL is an automatic noise limiter, which reduces impulse noise, such as noisy car ignitions. There may also be a switch to allow you to immediately switch to emergency channel 9 or commonly used channel 19. There may also be a switch to allow you to use the CB set as a public address amplifier. This is handy when the set is mounted in a car or truck.

Some sets will also have an *RF gain control*. An RF gain control is used in conjunction with the AF gain (AUDIO gain) to prevent the receiver audio from "overloading" with strong signals. The RF gain control controls the gain of the RF amplifier section of the CB receiver. This is the electronic section that amplifies the incoming signal before it is converted into the *intermediate frequency* used in receiver superheterodyne sets.

Sensitivity

Sensitivity, the ability to receive weak signals, is not a problem in modern HF receivers and is not usually a problem in CB sets. A CB set costing $180 instead of $75 will probably have about the same sensitivity as the less expensive set.

Single-Sideband Transmission and Reception

Most CB operation is currently in AM mode, the same modulation technique used in the AM broadcast band. However, there is a better method, called *single-sideband* (SSB) transmission. AM transmission has a carrier and two sidebands that echo the 3-kHz frequencies required for recognizable voice communication, making the bandwidth of the AM signal about 6-kHz wide. In SSB, the carrier and one of the sidebands is filtered out, leaving the SSB signal only about 3-kHz wide. Instead of wasting energy with the carrier and two sidebands, only one sideband is amplified and transmitted. The result is a signal that can "punch through" interfering stations, an important factor on the CB band, which has a tendency to be incredibly crowded, especially if the "skip" (long-distance stations) is coming in.

On a SSB CB set (see Figure 8-2), there is probably a three-position switch that selects either the upper or lower sideband for SSB operation (USB or LSB), or the AM mode. Which sideband is selected, upper or lower, affects tuning and selectivity of the received signal. If the wrong sideband is selected for receiving, it will be rejected and the signal will almost disappear due to the receiver's selectivity. The "wrong" sideband is the one opposite from the one used by the transmitting station.

Figure 8-2.
CB SSB Transceiver
Courtesy of Radio Shack,
A Division of Tandy Corporation

A clarifier control is used on many SSB CB sets when in SSB mode. This control actually adjusts the frequency of the internal *beat frequency oscillator* that performs the reinsertion of the carrier and allows SSB reception. All CB transmitters operate on about the same frequency, but even a small percentage variation may result in several kHz difference between two CB transmitters. The clarifier turns the SSB reception from something sounding much like Donald Duck to reasonable reception.

Power Supplies

Many CB sets are installed in cars and trucks. In these cases, the battery/alternator of the car or truck supplies the necessary dc power. When these sets are to be used in a base station, however, an external power supply must be used. This power supply converts 110 volts ac from the wall socket into 13.8 volts dc, which is then connected to the CB set. A regulated dc power supply that supplies 2.5 amps is sufficient to power the CB set.

Some *base-station* sets have a built in power supply so that the CB transceiver operates directly from the 110 vac supply.

CB Antennas

Many CB antennas are used in mobile (car or truck) installations (see Figure 8-3). There are a variety of antennas for mobile use, and all of them are designed to simply plug into the back of the CB set. If the antenna is properly designed, it will be a good "match" to the electrical characteristics of the CB set.

When a base station is used, the situation may be a little different. A greater variety of antennas can be used (see Chapter 11), and the *impedance match* may not be as close between the set and antenna as in the mobile installation. The match depends upon a variety of factors, including antenna design, feedline type, height of the antenna above ground, the quality of an electrical ground, and so forth.

In both cases, a base station or mobile operation, a *field-strength* or *SWR* meter (see Figure 8-4) can be used to get optimum performance from the CB set and antenna. The field-strength meter measures the strength of the radiated signal. By walking around a mobile or fixed antenna, the strength of the signal can be determined and even a radiation pattern can be drawn. The SWR meter is inserted in the antenna feedline and measures how much power is lost due to a mismatch between the CB set output and antenna impedance.

Many sets also include a built-in "power meter" represented by five LED indicator lights that show the level of output power.

Hand-Held CB Transceivers

The CB sets we've been discussing are all units designed to be mounted under the dash or placed on a table for fixed station operation. There is

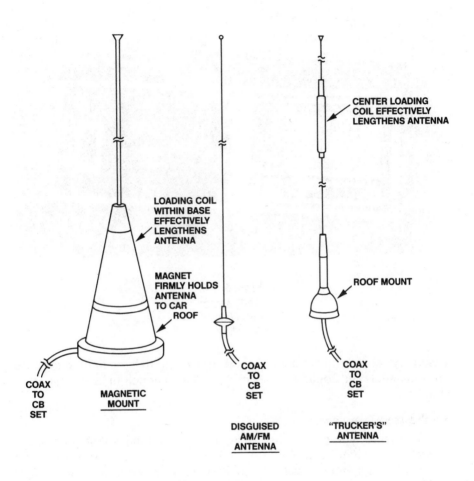

Figure 8-3.
Mobile CB Installation

another class of 11-meter CB sets that are "walkie-talkies", small hand-held units with a short telescoping antenna (see Figure 8-5). These sets come in two basic types—one uses *crystals* and the does not.

Crystal-Controlled Transceivers

A crystal is a thin slab of quartz about the size of a postage stamp. For each channel of a CB transceiver, two crystals are used, one for transmit and one for receive. In those walkie-talkies that use crystals, from one to six or more channels may be possible. You might want to use channel 9 for emergency use, channel 19 for calling, and a channel of your choice that is not used much in your area, for example. In this case, you'd require three

Figure 8-4.
SWR Meter
Courtesy of Radio Shack,
A Division of Tandy Corporation

sets of crystals, costing about $15 total. You would then be limited to those three channels and could not transmit on other channels or even hear other channels.

Synthesized Transceivers

The same type of circuitry is used in walkie-talkies that do not use crystals as is found in mobile or fixed station CB sets. In these sets the frequencies required for all 40 channels are *synthesized* by adding together and subtracting frequencies electronically. Depending upon the design, either multiple crystal oscillators or an electronic circuit called a *phased locked loop* is used. The result is the same — a set of discrete frequencies that are switch selectable. Both types provide coverage of all 40 channels without crystals, except for those built into the synthesis circuitry.

As you might expect, the cost of the synthesized walkie-talkies is greater, but there is a decided advantage in having all 40 channels available without having to add crystals for each channel desired.

Other Options

Both types of walkie-talkies usually offer a number of features which may vary from set to set. *Auto-modulation* ensures that the transmitter is modulated at the optimum level — it's a type of automatic volume control for the transmitter, much the same as on small tape recorders. A *ceramic filter* increases the *selectivity* of the receiver and helps eliminate adjacent channel interference. Squelch capability is found on most sets. A *separate*

Figure 8-5.
CB Walkie Talkie
Courtesy of Radio Shack,
A Division of Tandy Corporation

speaker and *microphone* option in addition to the built-in speaker and microphone are usually found on the more expensive sets. An e*arphone jack* may be included on some sets for privacy. Some sets have a *output power switch* that enables a lower-power transmitter output when communicating over shorter distances—this extends battery life. An *external antenna* jack may be available to increase the range of the transmitter by a more efficient antenna than the telescoping antenna that comes with the unit. Another antenna option is a "rubber ducky" type antenna—a short flexible unit that is more convenient than the fully extended telescoping antenna and has about the same performance. A *battery charger* may also be offered for recharging ni-cad batteries.

Walkie-Talkie Range

Both the sets using crystals and the synthesized sets operate at power inputs of up to five watts. Because the antennas are a little more of a compromise over a fixed or mobile station, the range of the walkie-talkies is not usually as great. However, a five-watt walkie-talkie can easily cover a few miles in conditions without interference, and actually could be used to contact stations across the United States if 11-meter conditions were right (however, the FCC does not like CB operators to operate in this mode!).

For Higher Power...

There are a number of CB operators that have illegally added *linear amplifiers* to their basic CB rigs and are operating with transmitters of hundreds of watts or more. This is in clear violation of the charter of CB, but it is not an uncommon occurrence. If you have those types of thoughts, why not look to getting an amateur radio license? There's a great deal more room in the amateur bands than in the 40 CB channels!

Chapter 9.
Amateur Radio Equipment

In this chapter we'll look at some of the currently available amateur radio equipment. Some hams have built all of their own equipment, including receivers. In the past, it was customary for a ham to build his own transmitter and buy a commercially available receiver. Today, older hams decry the "appliance operators" who buy off-the-shelf equipment, but it's hard reality that such equipment is superb. It would be a rare ham who could build equipment that would do the same things as commercially available equipment.

Transceivers Vs. Separate Receivers and Transmitters

Much ham equipment now is a combination transmitter and receiver called a "transceiver" (see Figure 9-1). Most ham operation involves transmitting and receiving on the same band. It's logical, therefore, for the receiver and transmitter to share some of the same circuitry. However, some hams prefer a separate receiver and transmitter, or may even have several receivers and/or transmitters. We'll discuss each unit separately and then describe some typical transceivers.

Figure 9-1.
Amateur Transceiver
Courtesy Trio-Kenwood
Communications

MF and HF Amateur Receivers

Amateur receivers are characterized by a number of factors. We'll try to put them in order of importance in the following discussion.

Coverage

First and foremost, the receiver should cover the amateur bands! Some older equipment will cover only the 160-, 80-, 40-, 20-, 15-, and 10-meter bands, as the newer 30- and 12-meter bands were not available during their time of manufacture. In some cases, newer equipment will cover the 30- and 12-meter bands only with an optional board or circuitry.

In addition to covering the amateur bands, it is nice to have the capability to cover WWV and WWVH broadcasts on 5, 10, 15, and 20 meters for current time and also for frequency calibration (aligning a transmitter's frequency).

BFO

As mentioned in other chapters, an amateur MF and HF receiver must have a beat frequency oscillator (BFO) to tune in CW, SSB, RTTY, and other amateur broadcasts. If a receiver does not have a BFO, it is of little use on the MF and HF ham bands.

RF Gain Control

In addition to an audio gain control, an amateur receiver must have an RF (radio frequency) gain control. An RF gain control controls the amplification in the radio-frequency amplifier and prevents overloading of the circuitry on strong signals. The proper way to tune in a CW signal, for example, is to turn up the AF gain to a strong level and then adjust the RF gain for a comfortable listening level. SSB tuning is similar.

Selectivity

One of the most important characteristics of an amateur receiver is *selectivity,* much more so than in a shortwave receiver. Selectivity is the ability of the receiver to tune in a single signal and reject all others. In receivers with poor selectivity, adjacent signals will sound nearly as loud as the signal to which you are tuned, or a more powerful adjacent signal will overpower the weaker signal you are trying to hear, as shown in Figure 9-2.

A selective receiver is tuned to one spot on the dial as shown in the figure and adjacent signals are rejected. More expensive receivers have variable selectivity. For SSB transmissions, the selectivity may be set to about 2.4 kHz, to allow for passing all voice frequencies up to 2400 Hz. (Tighter selectivity makes the voice unreadable.) For CW reception, the selectivity can be adjusted to 500 Hz or even less. CW reception doesn't require that a band of frequencies are passed, but only that a single frequency is passed. (Even so, it has a finite bandwidth dependent upon the

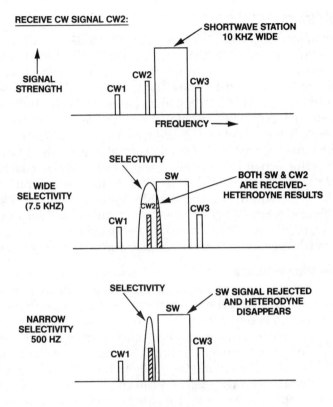

Figure 9-2.
Selectivity in an Amateur Receiver

code speed.) *Crystal filters,* fairly expensive selective devices, are used to change the selectivity.

Most receivers not only have good selectivity, but enhance the rejection of unwanted signals by filtering. In filtering, an interfering signal is rejected by a filter that sharply rejects a specific frequency (a "notch filter") or enhances the signal being received.

Sensitivity

Sensitivity is usually not a problem with modern receivers. Sensitivity refers to the ability to receive weak signals and is measured in microvolts of received signal. Good sensitivity for amateur band SSB reception is on the order of 0.25 microvolt for a 10-db signal-to-noise ratio on HF bands. This means that a signal of 0.25 microvolts at the antenna terminals will produce an audio output that is 10 decibels higher than the noise level of the receiver. A decibel is the smallest change in audio level that can be detected under normal conditions.

Variable Modes

Most amateur receivers will have a variable mode control, allowing you to select either CW, AM, FM, LSB, or USB. The CW and AM modes are the CW and AM we have been discussing. The FM mode is not *wide-band* FM, as is used in the VHF and UHF bands, but a version called *narrow-band* FM (NBFM) used on the MF and HF bands. Little narrow-band FM is used in these bands, however. The LSB and USB modes are extremely important. They refer to which sideband is used in a single sideband signal. AM transmission has a carrier and two sidebands that echo the 3-kHz frequencies required for recognizable voice communication, making the bandwidth of the AM signal about 6-kHz wide. In SSB, the carrier and one of the sidebands is filtered out, leaving the SSB signal only about 3-kHz wide. Which sideband is left, upper or lower, affects tuning and selectivity of the received signal. If the wrong sideband is selected for receiving, it will be rejected and the signal will almost disappear due to the receiver's selectivity.

Analog Vs. Digital Tuning

There are two distinct types of tuning available in amateur receivers. Older receivers use *analog* tuning. In this type of tuning, different coils are manually switched to select the band (80 meters, 40 meters, etc.). After the band has been selected, a capacitor or other electronic part is rotated to change the received frequency within the band. A readout dial with a pointer or log scale is linked mechanically to the capacitor to provide the frequency at which a signal is being received.

Newer receivers, however, *synthesize* the frequencies used in receiving signals. (In *all* sophisticated receivers a local oscillator is used to mix with a received signal to generate a new frequency, which is then amplified and converted to audio.) Synthesis involves tuning a *voltage controlled oscillator,* or VCO, by electrical means. The VCO frequency can be changed easily by applying a new voltage. Several VCOs may be alternately used. A *phase locked loop* is used to stabilize the frequency output. This method of tuning can be linked very easily to a digital readout, typically an *LCD* or liquid crystal display—the same type of display you'll find on digital clocks or watches. Instead of a pointer on a dial, these receiver types use a digital readout for the received frequency.

Synthesized receivers with digital tuning lend themselves to all kinds of tuning tricks. Scanning can be done by changing the frequency an increment at a time. This amounts to a new "channel" every 100 cycles. A scan on the 20-meter band would display 14.200.0 (14,200,000 Hz), then 14.200.1 (14,200,100 Hz), then 14.200.2 (14,200,200 Hz), and so forth. Given the proper electronics, specific frequencies can be entered with a few control panel buttons for scanning of a set of frequencies. You might scan between 14,200,100, 14,200,800, and 14,200,600 Hz in that order, for example. You could also enter widely different frequencies on different bands and with the flick of a button, rapidly switch between the 40-meter CW band and the 75-meter phone band. Finally, if you had a small computer, you could even use the computer to change the frequencies with the proper connections (usually provided by the receiver manufacturer, but not by the computer manufacturer).

Synthesized receivers tend to be more expensive than their analog counterparts. There are some fine analog receivers that are just as selective and well engineered as any synthesized receiver, but the trend is definitely towards synthesized digital receivers.

Other Receiver Features

Stability of receivers is not as much of a problem as it once was. A stable receiver doesn't change frequency at the slightest vibration. It also doesn't change frequency much as it heats up. Older receivers, especially the ones that used vacuum tubes (remember those?) were susceptible to drift as the receiver heated up.

Antenna tuners allow a wide range of antennas to be connected to the receiver. Receivers without antenna tuners are usually limited to a *50—to 75-ohm* antenna input, the characteristic *impedance* (see Chapter 11) of a half-wave dipole and other common antenna types. Not having an antenna tuner doesn't mean you won't be able to receive stations, it just means that the antenna you are connecting to may not be transferring the signal it receives without power loss.

Most amateur receivers have more than enough audio power. Three watts of audio, for example, is more than adequate for most amateur work. A headphone jack and internal speaker is usually provided. External speakers are usually an option and match the case of the receiver. The external speaker faces outward, which makes communications more understandable than an internal speaker that faces towards the top or side of the receiver.

A *squelch* control enables the audio of the receiver only when a signal is present. Without the squelch, you'll hear the continual hiss and crash of background noise, a severe problem on MF and HF bands. With the squelch, you'll hear nothing unless there is a station strong enough to "override the squelch". The squelch level is settable to strong or weak signals. Squelch, however, is normally more usable on the VHF and UHF bands where there is less variation in the received signal level.

S-meters in receivers show the strength of the received signal. They are not a necessity, but a convenient feature to have.

MF and HF Amateur Transmitters

There are several types of amateur transmitters. Older transmitters are separate units, but newer transmitters are usually integrated with a receiver into a *transceiver*. Novice transmitters are CW only transmitters or transceivers. All transmitters, whether in transceivers or stand-alone units, have the same characteristics, which we'll describe in the following discussion.

Power

Amateur regulations permit a maximum power of 1000 watts on AM or CW transmissions. SSB transmitters are allowed a *peak envelope power* (PEP) of 1500 watts. The output power amounts to the same thing regardless of the mode. How much power is necessary? There are certainly amateurs that are running absolute legal power (and more). There are also amateurs, however, that are using QRP transmitters (see Figure 9-3) of less than five watts input power and enjoying themselves immensely!

Figure 9-3.
Low-Power (QRP) Transceiver
Courtesy Heath Company

It is possible to become a DX Century Club member (100 countries contacted) with only a 5-watt CW transmitter and to contact other countries on SSB phone with a 20-watt transceiver. However, on crowded competitive bands, such as 20 meters, it takes patience and fortitude to operate with low power. A reasonable operating power that can be used on all bands with good results is 75 to 200 watts.

Doubling the power results in a received signal that is 3 decibels stronger. A decibel is the the smallest change in audio level that can just be detected under ideal conditions. Increasing transmitter power from 100 to 200 watts, therefore, produces a change in the received signal by a relatively small amount—not double the strength, but just three increments of loudness. Doubling the power again from 200 to 400 watts produces an equivalent change. Doubling the power from 400 to 800 watts produces the same change in received signal. The point is that having maximum power in a transmitter does not produce a signal that is *overwhelming* compared to a moderately powered transmitter.

Another factor affecting the received signal is the transmitter antenna system. Having a three-element "beam" antenna rather than a half-wave dipole antenna (see Chapter 11) will result in more of a perceived increase in the received signal then increasing transmitter power four times, say from 100 to 400 watts!

Frequency Selection

Older Novice transmitters have provisions for *frequency crystals,* postage stamp-sized slabs of quartz crystal that determine the operating frequency. Newer Novice regulations permit variable-frequency-oscillators (VFOs) to permit selecting any frequency within a band range.

Older transmitters were *narrow-band amplifiers* that required somewhat elaborate tuning steps to properly tune the output power circuits. Newer transmitters are *wide-band* designs that simply require a reasonably matched antenna system (or an optional antenna tuner). One simply switches to the proper frequency.

As in the case of new receivers, the new transmitter designs use synthesized frequencies, especially in the case of transceivers, in which the receiver and transmitter share frequency generation circuits. Transmitting frequencies can be programmed as well as receiver frequencies. Older transmitters, by contrast, are tuned manually, much in the same fashion as analog receivers—a sliding dial scan mechanically linked to the tuning capacitor.

Older transmitters will not have the newer amateur bands and will probably not have the provision for adding them.

Variable Modes

A general purpose amateur transmitter will have CW, AM, and SSB transmitting capability, with selection of upper or lower sideband on SSB. The CW mode may offer *break-in keying,* a feature in which the receiver can be heard in-between key closures, or at least between words. The AM and SSB voice modes will offer a *VOX,* or voice-actuated transmit feature in which the transmitter is turned on and off automatically by the operator's voice.

Transceivers

A modern amateur transceiver employs the best and most sophisticated features found in receivers and transmitters. The frequency synthesis circuits are shared by the receiver and transmitter alike. As the receiver is scanned across the amateur band, the transmitter tracks the receiving frequency, allowing immediate response to the received station. This is very handy in contests, DX (distance) work, or just casual contacts in crowded bands. The receiver has a feature called *receiver incremental tuning* (RIT), which allows the received frequency to be offset a few kHz so that the band can be scanned in the immediate region. The transmitter is a broadband amplifier, requiring little or no tuning. A combination S-meter and transmitter power and modulation meter is used both for reception and transmitting. The transceiver usually has provision for radio RTTY as well, an *FSK* (frequency shift keying) mode that enables the frequency to be rapidly shifted based upon the on-off radio teleprinter signals input from external equipment. Some transceivers come with built-in antenna tuners and some require an external antenna tuning unit. The antenna tuner is not necessary with a single-band properly matched antenna, but is usually a necessity in the average amateur station.

VHF and UHF Amateur Equipment

VHF and UHF equipment is almost always of the transceiver type, where the receiver and transmitter are integrated into a single unit. There are two basic types of transceivers, a base station unit, which may also be used for mobile operation, and a hand-held HT (walkie talkie) that can clip onto a belt or be carried in one hand (see Figure 9-4).

Figure 9-4.
HT Amateur Transceiver
Courtesy ICOM America

Most VHF and UHF communications are in FM (frequency modulation) mode, but some units (especially the base stations) have provision for CW and SSB as well.

Typical input power for the hand-held units is five watts and for the base units is from 25 to 70 watts. Much VHF and UHF activity is via repeaters (see

Chapter 2), so high transmitter power is not necessary. There are VHF and UHF enthusiasts that do much long-distance work involving meteor scatter and "Earth-Moon-Earth" transmissions using maximum power, however.

Transceivers for VHF and UHF generally cover one band, although two-band models are also popular. The most popular band covered is two meters (144 MHz), with the next most popular bands being 1 1/4 meters (220 MHz) and 3/4 meters (440 MHz).

Sensitivity and *selectivity* apply to the receiver portion of the transceiver just as in the case of MF and HF receivers.

Newer VHF and UHF transceivers *synthesize* their frequencies as in the case of the newer MF and HF ham gear. The readout is generally a liquid crystal display showing the last digits of the frequency band. A two-meter transceiver, for example, may display 6.970.1, representing 146,970,100 Hz on the band. Like their lower-frequency counterparts, the transceivers have *receiver incremental tuning* so that the received signal can be offset somewhat from the transmitting frequency. As in the case of the MF and HF transceivers, all kinds of options are allowed in setting up sequences of channels to be scanned or switched at the press of a button.

As many repeaters have controlled access by keying in a sequence of tones, many VHF and UHF transceivers incorporate a *DTMF pad* (Dual-tone multi-frequency pad) (see Figure 9-5). This pad generates tones equivalent to dial telephone tones which are then decoded for repeater access or for using the repeater in *autopatch* mode to connect to local telephone lines. One of the best-kept secrets of amateur radio (at least to the general public) is the access to a phone line via a repeater from a VHF or UHF rig in the car—an inexpensive car phone!

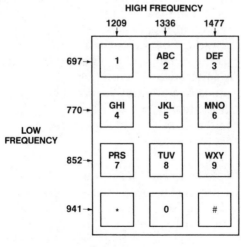

Figure 9-5.
DTMF Pad

Chapter 10.
VHF and UHF Receivers and Scanners

There is a wide range of equipment available for the VHF and UHF portion of the radio spectrum. Hand-held radios covering the NOAA weather frequencies, the aviation band (108—135 MHz), and VHF television audio are available for as little as $20. Larger portables that cover several bands with slide-rule type tuning are available in the under $100 range. *Scanners,* sophisticated receivers that automatically scan a wide range of VHF and UHF frequencies, are available from about $100 to $500 or more. We'll look at these types of receivers in this chapter and describe the features found on each.

Hand-held Receivers

Hand-held receivers (see Figure 10-1) usually cover one or two bands, have a small speaker and earphone jack, and have only two controls, one for volume, and one for tuning control. The unit is usually powered by a 9-volt battery. A telescoping antenna is used. A typical unit of this type covers the 108—to 135-MHz aircraft band and the AM broadcast band, and is the type of thing you might want to take to air shows or a local airport.

Reception from such a unit is not spectacular, as you might expect, but it is often more than adequate for local broadcasts. In my area, for example, I can receive both the transmissions from a local major airport, about 15 miles away, and from aircraft themselves.

The major disadvantage of such a unit is that it's difficult to find a specific frequency, as the tuning dial calibration is not that precise. Also, once you've carefully adjusted the tuning knob to a transmitting station, you will not be able to quickly and easily locate the second station without losing the location of the first.

These units are best used by children or in those cases in which you'll be monitoring one strong local station.

Larger Portables

A second type of portable receiver is a larger unit, typically eight by ten by three inches. This unit is also battery-powered, usually with four "C" cells or the equivalent, but also has provision for ac power (see Figure 10-2). Often these units will include four or five bands, switch selectable. Typical bands might be the aircraft band (108—135 MHz), VHF low band (30—50 MHz), VHF high band (144—178 MHz), the FM broadcast band (88—108

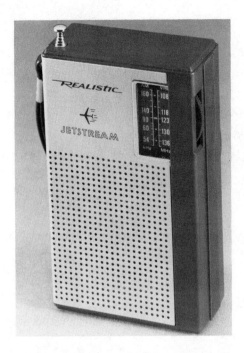

Figure 10-1.
Hand-held VHF Receiver
Courtesy of Radio Shack,
A Division of Tandy Corporation

MHz), and the AM broadcast band (550 KHz—1.5 MHz). Sometimes, VHF and/or UHF bands will be included with shortwave bands.

The reception with this type of receiver is usually much better than the hand-held unit. Most of these units have a slide-rule type dial that shows all frequency bands. Tuning is much easier with a unit of this type than a hand-held unit as the tuning control is usually geared down so that one revolution of the tuning knob moves the pointer only a short way across the dial. Sometimes there is also a fine tuning control which even makes it easier to zero in on a station.

A typical receiver of this type will have a band selector switch, tuning control, volume control, and sometimes a "squelch" control. The squelch control is used to turn off the audio when there is no station present to eliminate fatiguing radio noise. The squelch is set just beyond the point where the noise keeps the audio on—any station beyond that noise level will then "break the squelch" and turn on the audio.

Most units have a 3—to 3 1/2-inch speaker and an earphone jack. The larger speaker (compared to the hand-held unit) is a plus for good quality FM broadcast band reception.

A telescoping antenna about 16 inches long is normally used, but many units also include a jack for an optional external antenna. Usually the external antenna, even if it is a random length of wire, will improve reception noticeably.

Figure 10-2.
VHF Portable Receiver
Courtesy of Radio Shack,
A Division of Tandy Corporation

Scanners

The hand-held and portable receivers we've been discussing above use analog tuning. In this type of tuning, different coils are manually switched to select the band (VHF low, aircraft band, etc.). After the band has been selected, a capacitor or other electronic part is rotated to change the received frequency within the band. A readout dial with a pointer or log scale is linked mechanically to the capacitor to provide the frequency at which a signal is being received.

However, there's another type of VHF and UHF receiver which has become very popular in recent years, called a *scanner*. Scanners continually switch to a set of channels until a channel is found with a station that is transmitting. Since most VHF and UHF stations transmit intermittently, scanners can rapidly find an active channel without an operator having to continually move a tuning dial. Another advantage is that they can rapidly scan between two stations on different frequencies that are talking with each other to make the conversation appear as if it were a single channel.

One type of VHF and UHF scanner uses *frequency crystals* to determine the channel frequency (see Figure 10-3). A crystal is a thin slab of quartz

Figure 10-3.
Scanner with Crystals
Courtesy of Radio Shack,
A Division of Tandy Corporation

crystal about the size of a postage stamp. If you knew that police calls were on frequencies of 154.950, 155.430, 159.150, and 460.010 MHz in your area, for example, you might want to use four crystals with those frequencies in your scanner. The scanner would continuously cycle through the frequencies (channels), stopping on whatever channel had someone making a transmission. When the transmission was over, the scanner would continue the cycle until the next channel was active.

Typical scanners of this type scan four or more channels on one or more bands and allow mixing the bands and channels to be scanned—you might want to monitor 154.950 MHz on VHF high band and 460.010 MHz on UHF high band, for example. The channel selected is displayed on an LED lamp arranged in a row of eight (for an eight-channel scanner); for scanning, the LEDs would illuminate in sequence at the scanning rate, typically four to ten scans per second. The LED illuminated when the scanning stopped would be the channel on which the station was transmitting.

Scanners of this type usually have a volume control, a squelch control and a scanning mode selection, allowing a manual selection of the channel or a continuous scan. Both fixed station types and "walkie-talkie" versions usually have a telescoping antenna with provision for attaching an external antenna.

Synthesized Tuning

Another type of scanner (see Figure 10-4), about twice as expensive, uses a different type of tuning. This type synthesizes the frequencies used in receiving signals. Synthesis involves adding and subtracting frequencies by digital means or digitally controlling a *voltage controlled oscillator* (VCO) to generate the proper receiving frequency. This method of tuning can be linked very easily to a digital readout, typically an LCD (liquid crystal display)—the same type of display you'll find on digital clocks or watches. Instead of seeing a pointer on a dial representing a frequency, or an LED indicator lamp to indicate the channel, you'll see a digital readout representing the received frequency.

Figure 10-4.
Scanner with Synthesized Tuning
Courtesy of Radio Shack,
A Division of Tandy Corporation

Synthesized receivers with digital tuning lend themselves to all kinds of tuning tricks. Scanning can be done by changing the frequency an increment at a time. This amounts to a new "channel" every 5 kHz. A scan from 30 MHz would display 30.000 (30,000,000 Hz), then 30.005 (30,005,000 Hz), and so forth. Given the proper electronics, specific frequencies can be entered with a few control panel buttons for scanning of a set of frequencies. You might scan between 144,000,000, 144,200,000, and 144,380,000 Hz in that order, for example. You could also enter widely different frequencies on different bands and with the press of a button, rapidly switch between UHF high band and VHF low band, for instance.

The synthesized type of scanning can be incorporated in a hand-held scanner to provide a small, powerful scanner that can be used anywhere— the best of all worlds (see Figure 10-5).

Figure 10-5.
Hand-Held Scanner
Courtesy of Radio Shack,
A Division of Tandy Corporation

Scanner Attributes

Here are some of the attributes to look for in scanners.

Tuning Range

The lower-frequency range in scanners is usually 30 MHz, although some go as low as 25 MHz, providing coverage of the 11-meter CB band. The upper-frequency limit is usually 512 MHz, although some scanners go as high as 1300 MHz. Within that coverage, the frequencies are usually broken up into combinations of these bands:

- VHF low   30 - 50 MHz
- Six-meter amateur band   50 - 54 MHz
- VHF air   108 - 136 MHz
- Government   138 - 144 MHz
- Two-meter amateur band   144 - 148 MHz

- VHF high   148 - 174 MHz
- Amateur/Government   380 - 450 MHz
- UHF low   450 - 470 MHz
- UHF high   470 - 512 MHz

Some newer scanners provide continuous coverage of all channels between about 25 MHz and 512 MHz and even above.

Number of Frequencies The scanning steps are usually 5 kHz in the lower frequencies and 25 kHz in the very high frequencies, allowing tens of thousands of individual channels that may be accessed! Needless to say, at the rate of eight to ten channels per second, it takes many minutes to scan a 5-MHz wide band. A better solution is provided by programmable scanning.

Programmable Scanning When a scanner is advertised as a "300-Channel" scanner, the manufacturer is not referring to the number of frequency channels that can be scanned. Instead, he is referring to the number of individual channels that can be stored in the memory or program of the scanner. A 20-channel scanner, therefore, memorizes 20 frequencies such as the following:

Channel 1 - 139.055 MHz
Channel 2 - 140.010
Channel 3 - 43.5
Channel 4 - 152.75
Channel 5 - 480.35
Channel 6 - 112.3

.

.

Channel 20 - 53.5

As you can see from the sample, the frequencies do not have to be on the same band, nor do they have to be in any order. The channels are entered in the program mode of the scanner. In this mode, the numeric keypad on the scanner is used to enter each channel number and the frequency for the channel.

Once the channels are entered, they can be changed at any time. If you found out that the frequency of 480.35 was really a frequency of 480.25, for example, it would be an easy matter to reprogram channel 5 again without having to go through the entire sequence.

When power is turned off, you'd expect the channel programming to disappear. This is not the case. A battery in the scanner maintains the programming even when the ac power to the scanner is disrupted on purpose or by accident, so the channels will always remain programmed.

If you wanted to scan all 20 channels in our example, the entire 20 channels would be scanned at a typical rate of 8 channels per second. As soon as a signal was encountered on any of the channels, the scanner would stop and you'd hear the transmission. As soon as the transmission stopped, the scanner would continue with the next channel in sequence. At the end of the 20 channels, the entire sequence would start over again.

If you wanted to scan only a few channels, you could lock out those channels you didn't wish to hear by programming a lock out on that channel. The lock out would not destroy the frequency digits but would just signal the scan sequence to ignore that channel for the time being.

If you wanted to pause at any channel when you heard a transmission, you could program a delay into any of the channels. This would delay for a few seconds before scanning was resumed after the transmission ended. Without the delay, the scanning would immediately resume after transmission, and on short transmissions might not give you enough time to pause manually.

In addition to using the preprogrammed sequence, you could set an upper—and lower-frequency limit for scanning. The scanner would then scan that frequency range in five-kHz (or 25-kHz) steps in a regular scanning sequence. You can also monitor any channel you have programmed by manually selecting the channel and then advancing to the next channel(s).

Scanners started out with four, then eight, then 100, and then hundreds of programmable channels! Current models allow about 300 separate channels to be programmed. In addition to simply programming the channels manually, you can add new channels as you encounter them, building up a list in scanner memory of the ones you would most like to monitor. The channels are arranged in "banks" for convenience.

Other Scanner Features

Most programmable scanners have the numeric keypad for channel number and frequency, an operating keypad, a volume control, a squelch control, and an LCD display (see Figure 10-6). Jacks are usually available on the back for external speaker, external antenna, and (sometimes) tape recorder. All scanners have a telescoping antenna built in, but an external antenna should definitely be considered.

A scanner is a receiver in spite of the programmable glitch. For this reason, some of the electronic specifications of the scanner should be considered when evaluating scanners. Two of the qualities to consider are selectivity and *sensitivity*.

Selectivity is the ability of the scanner to separate adjacent channels. Although this is not as much of a problem as on the MF and HF bands, the scanner should have sufficient selectivity so that adjacent channel transmissions are not heard. If you are to be scanning the amateur VHF and UHF bands, this is particularly important, as channels there are not as standardized as for other services in the VHF and UHF region.

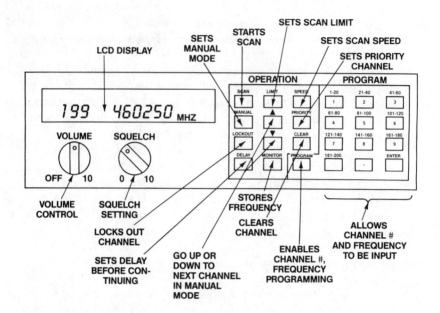

Figure 10-6.
Scanner Control Pad

Sensitivity is the ability of the scanner to receive weak signals. Most VHF and UHF transmissions are line-of-sight, but a scanner should still have sufficient sensitivity to receive weak signals. Again, this is most important on the amateur bands, but could also be the case if you were doing specialized receiving, such as receiving satellite transmissions.

Amateur Band Scanners

If you are interested in scanning the amateur bands, then you might want to consider an amateur transceiver. Transceivers consist of a transmitter and receiver. Newer transceivers have many of the features of receiving scanners and many more besides. Although they will only cover a specific VHF or UHF amateur band, or possibly two or three bands, they are an excellent choice for that coverage. See Chapter 9.

Chapter 11.
Antennas for Shortwave, CB, VHF, and UHF

Most receivers come with a built-in telescoping antenna which pulls out of the receiver. In many cases, this is more than adequate for good reception. However, in just about every case, adding an *external* antenna will dramatically increase the signal levels of a selected band of frequencies for any type of receiver. Many antennas are very inexpensive, especially the types used for reception on the shortwave or HF bands. Low-cost materials, or antennas themselves, can be found at any Radio Shack store.

Simple Shortwave or HF Antennas

Just about any random length of wire can be added to a receiving antenna to increase performance. The wire can be virtually any size, from #30 (a very thin wire) to #22 or less (#22 is a wire typically used for electronic wiring). The minute currents flowing through receiving antenna wire do not call for the wire diameters used for most electrical applications.

Generally, the more wire that is strung from the receiver and the higher that wire is, the better, within limits. (This is especially true for reception of LF and ELF frequencies.) You might drape a wire around your attic, for example, and lead it down to a room where you keep your receiver. The antenna does not have to be outside the house, since radio waves can penetrate non-metallic buildings quite easily.

If you want optimum performance, though, an antenna outside your house and in the clear will help give it to you. Typical antennas might be strung from a window to the eaves of a house, or from a window to a nearby tree. However, if you live in an area with thunderstorms, realize that any outside wire is susceptible to not only a direct strike with lightning, but induced, powerful currents for a nearby lightning strike. Read the section at the end of this chapter entitled *Lightning Protection*.

FOR YOUR OWN SAFETY

Never route antennas near electrical power lines or where high voltages (including household wiring) might come in contact with any part of the antenna. Always exercise care and common sense when installing antennas on rooftops and other high places.

The connections required for a receiving antenna are usually through a jack in the back of the receiver, as shown in Figure 11-1. There are three types of plugs that fit these jacks in common use—the RCA type, the PL-259 type, and the Motorola type. Converters are available from Radio Shack for connecting one type of plug to another. You might want to connect a PL-259 plug on the end of a coaxial cable to a Motorola plug for a scanner, for example, and there is such a converter.

RCA-TYPE PLUG USED ON HAND-HELD CB'S

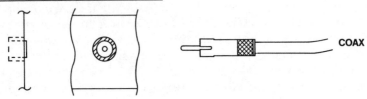

PL-259 PLUG USED ON FIXED OR MOBILE CB'S, LARGER RECEIVERS, AND TRANSCEIVERS

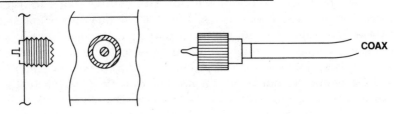

MOTOROLA PLUG USED ON SCANNERS, VHF/UHF EQUIPMENT

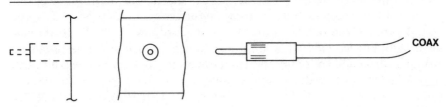

Figure 11-1.
Antenna Plugs and Jacks

Antenna Theory

Radio waves are emitted from a simple radio antenna in a doughnut shape as shown in Figure 11-2. We say from a "simple" antenna, because many antennas for large installations are not simple. Antennas may be *horizontally* or *vertically polarized.* Horizontally polarized antennas have the main *radiating element* of the antenna running lengthwise compared to the

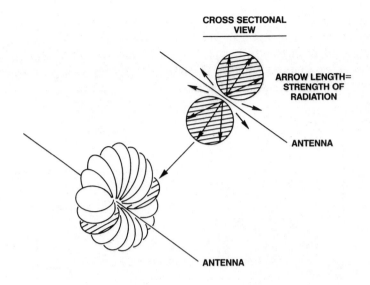

CROSS SECTIONAL
VIEW

ARROW LENGTH=
STRENGTH OF
RADIATION

ANTENNA

ANTENNA

Figure 11-2.
Radio Wave Propagation

ground. Vertically polarized antennas have a vertical radiating element. Most antennas used in cars are vertically polarized. Many antenna used on the HF bands are horizontally polarized.

For line-of-sight communications (VHF and UHF and above) best reception results will occur when the polarization of the transmitting and receiving antenna is the same. For example, if the transmitting antenna is vertically polarized, the receiving antenna will work best if it is also vertically polarized. For MF and HF antennas polarization is not as critical, as the signal loses some of its orientation as it travels through space and is reflected by the ionosphere, possibly several times.

A Simple Dipole

Note in the figure that the simple dipole antenna is *directional.* The weakest signals are transmitted off the ends of the antenna. The strongest signals are transmitted broadside to the antenna.

When the antenna is a vertical antenna, the same doughnut-shaped pattern is present, but the antenna exhibits a more or less omnidirectional radiation pattern, radiating in all directions.

The most simple antenna is one-half wavelength of the center of the band of frequencies to be covered, assuming that the band is fairly narrow, as is the case for the 11-meter CB band, amateur bands, or a single shortwave band.

Radio waves travel at the speed of light, 186,410 miles per second or 186,410 x 5280 = 984,244,000 feet per second. The distance from crest to crest of a radio wave (see Figure 11-3) is one complete cycle of the wave. The number of cycles per second (Hz) is the frequency of the wave. The length of each cycle (the *wavelength*) in feet is therefore equal to

984/ f

where f is the frequency in MHz.

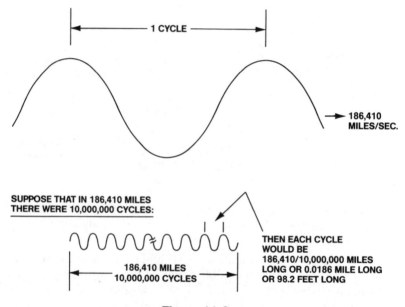

Figure 11-3.
Radio Wavelength

The dipole antenna uses a half wavelength of the center frequency of the band, however, so the formula becomes

half wavelength = 492/ f

where f is the frequency in MHz.

The half-wave dipole appears as shown in Figure 11-4. It is *center-fed* with 52-ohm coaxial cable. The conducting wire for receiving can be any wire. (The author once used fine, almost invisible #30 wire at a college dorm where antennas were not allowed, but forgot that ice forms during the winter!) For receiving purposes, any small-diameter coaxial cable can be used, such as RG-58/U (Radio Shack 276-1326). The connections to the wire should be soldered. The receiver end is connected with a coaxial connector that fits your specific receiver.

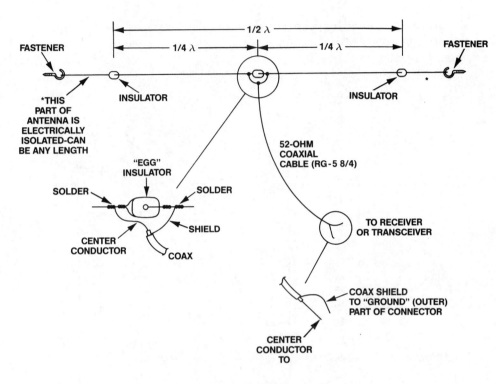

Figure 11-4.
Half-Wave Dipole

For best results, the antenna should be greater than one-half wavelength and high and clear of obstructions.

Typical Antenna Lengths

To give you an idea of how long a half-wave dipole is at various frequencies, look at Figure 11-5. It shows a graph that plots the length of half-wavelength antennas for frequencies of 3 MHz to 300 MHz. Lengths are in feet or inches.

At 4 MHz (80 meters), a half-wave antenna is 123 feet long. For a 9.5-MHz shortwave signal, a half-wave antenna is 52 feet long. At 30 MHz, a half-wave antenna is 16.4 feet long. At 144 MHz (2-meter band), a half-wave antenna is 40.5 inches long.

Another way to figure the approximate length of a half-wave antenna is to divide the band wavelength in meters by two. A 40-meter half-wave antenna is about 20 meters long (a meter is 39.37 inches).

When an antenna is cut for a specific frequency, it will perform fairly well over the entire band, provided the band is not too wide. A 40-meter amateur antenna will work well for 7 MHz to 7.3 MHz if cut for 7.15 MHz. If you know beforehand that you'll be receiving signals in the phone portion of the band at about 7.25 MHz, however, use that frequency in determining antenna length.

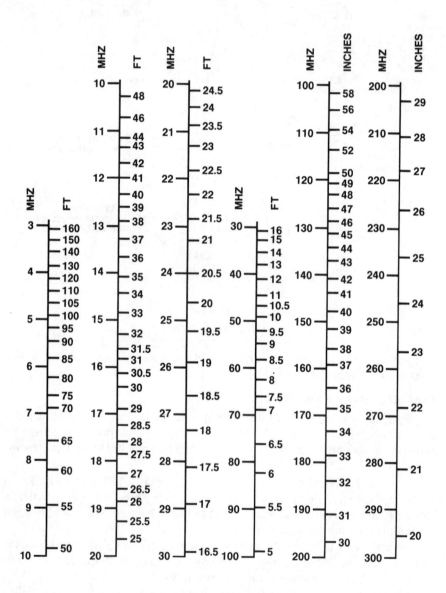

Figure 11-5.
Half Wavelength Vs. Frequency

A Quarter-Wave Vertical Antenna

An antenna similar to the half-wave antenna can be made by standing the antenna on end. One configuration of this antenna uses the entire length of the antenna, as shown in Figure 11-6. A more common type of antenna, however, uses either ground-plane *radials,* an earth ground, or an artificial ground such as a car body, as shown in the figure.

This antenna is normally fed with 52-ohm coaxial cable such as RG-58/U (Radio Shack 276-1326). For receiving purposes, a lightweight coax can be used with no problem. At VHF frequencies, a heavier coaxial cable should be used to avoid excessive signal losses — RG-8/U or RG-8/M is recommended.

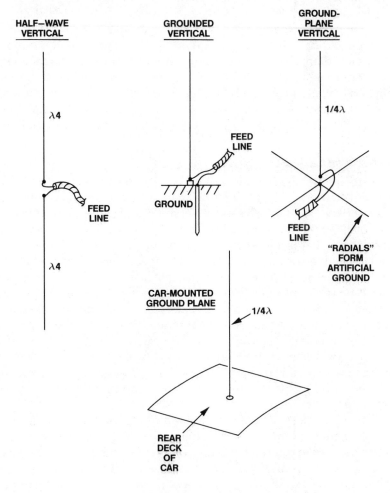

Figure 11-6.
Vertical Antennas

The overall antenna length for a quarter-wavelength vertical antenna is just one-half of that shown in Figure 11-5. A 2-meter antenna becomes about half a meter long (about 20 inches long), therefore, a much easier length to handle.

As in the case of the half-wave dipole, suitable lightning protection should be used.

Why Whip Antennas Are Shorter Than You'd Think

Most CB, VHF, and UHF antennas are much shorter than you'd expect a quarter-wave length antenna to be. Typical mobile CB antennas, for example, would be about 11/4 meters (108 inches) but are often about 37 to 48 inches long. The reason for this is that many mobile, VHF, and UHF antennas use a *loading coil.* A loading coil is an inductance, or wire in the shape of a coil, that electrically lengthens an antenna. The antenna can therefore be made shorter than a full-sized antenna without sacrificing too much in the way of performance. A "rubber ducky" antenna with flexible whip is of the loading-coil type and is much shorter than even the typical telescoping antenna. It is possible to make your own loading coils and to install them in any type of antenna, including horizontally polarized HF antennas.

Other Antenna Types

There are literally hundreds of other antenna types that can be made with simple materials. Unfortunately, many of these antennas must be fed with something other than 52—to 72-ohm coaxial cable. Typical feed lines consist of 300-ohm twin lead and 600-ohm open-wire line (two wires spaced by insulators). If the proper feed line is not used, an imbalance in the antenna system results with a portion of the feed line becoming part of the antenna. In the ideal antenna system, all of the energy is received (or transmitted) in the antenna proper and not in the feed line.

Many newer receivers and transceivers have a set *output impedance* of about 50 ohms and are geared to an antenna system with the same impedance. Some equipment has an antenna tuner, which will *match* a different impedance feed line to the 50-ohm connection on the equipment. If an antenna tuner is not available, it is possible to buy add-on antenna tuners which perform the matching function, either for transmitters or receivers or both (transceivers).

One of the most popular antenna types for the higher frequency HF bands (20 meters, 15 meters, and 10 meters), VHF, and UHF is a *beam.* This antenna is shown in Figure 11-7. It uses one element as a *driven element* and additional reflectors and directors that have no direct connection to the feed line. Beams provide great improvements over half-wave dipoles, increasing the level of a received signal about four times for a three-element version.

Beams are highly directional as well. A common television antenna is a version of a beam antenna.

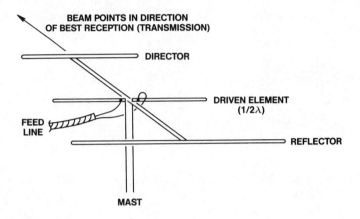

Figure 11-7.
Beam Antenna

On the HF bands, there are other interesting antennas. A *trapped* antenna is used on amateur or shortwave bands for transmission and reception on several bands about equally well. The traps are cylindrical pieces that are inserted in the center of each leg of the antenna, as shown in Figure 11-8. The traps contain a coil and capacitor in parallel. The traps effectively cut off the ends of the antennas on a high-frequency band, have no effect on an intermediate band, and load the antenna to make it electrically longer on a lower-frequency band.

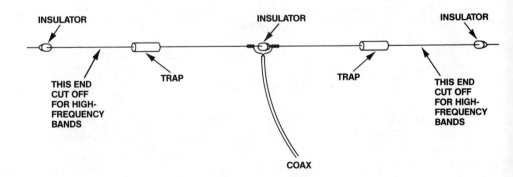

Figure 11-8.
Trapped Antenna

A multiple-band antenna can be used on several amateur or shortwave bands. It combines several antennas with a single feed point, as shown in Figure 11-9. In this case the individual legs are cut to the proper lengths based upon the bands to be covered. The bands should not be multiples of each other.

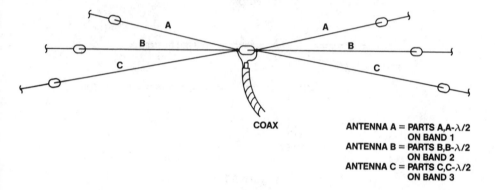

ANTENNA A = PARTS A,A-λ/2
ON BAND 1
ANTENNA B = PARTS B,B-λ/2
ON BAND 2
ANTENNA C = PARTS C,C-λ/2
ON BAND 3

Figure 11-9.
Multi-Band Antenna

A long-wire antenna (Figure 11-10) is a center—or end-fed antenna that is a integral number of half-wavelengths long. This type of antenna works well on amateur bands which are frequency multiples of each other—80, 40, 20, and 10. It doesn't work as well for multiple shortwave bands, which are generally not multiples of each other in frequency.

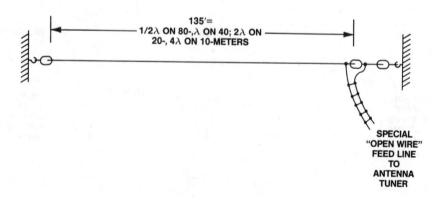

Figure 11-10.
Long-Wire Antenna

A number of amateurs radio operators and even some SWLs get very serious about their hobby. For those afficianados, there are some powerful antenna configurations that can be used. A v or rhombic antenna may be used on HF bands to get substantial signal gains on receiving or transmitting. In the v configuration, the antenna is a tight v shape, many wavelengths long, and aimed at the area of interest. For example, if the far east is of interest, the open portion of the v is aimed in a westerly direction. The rhombic antenna is similar, but the legs of one v are joined by another v section to form a rhombic or diamond shape. These antennas are shown in Figure 11-11.

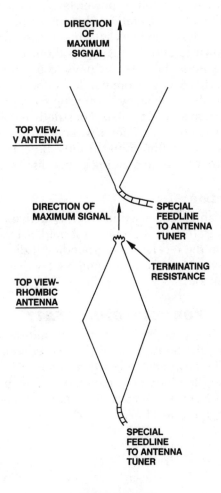

DIRECTION
OF
MAXIMUM
SIGNAL

TOP VIEW-
V ANTENNA

DIRECTION OF
MAXIMUM SIGNAL

SPECIAL
FEEDLINE
TO ANTENNA
TUNER

TERMINATING
RESISTANCE

TOP VIEW-
RHOMBIC
ANTENNA

SPECIAL
FEEDLINE
TO ANTENNA
TUNER

Figure 11-11.
V and Rhombic Antennas

Antennas and Propagation

When dealing with long distance reception or communication, it is handy to have a globe or global map that shows *great circle* headings. Radio waves radiate out from the source in straight lines. Although nothing can be done about fixed antennas, true headings are required for best reception for rotatable beam antennas for amateur or CB use.

Transmitting Antennas

The same basic antenna configurations can be used for both receiving and transmitting. However, transmitting antennas must be constructed of heavier materials if the transmitter power levels are above a QRP (low-power) level. For normal CB operation, the output power is considered a QRP power level as it is less than five watts. In this case the antenna wire can be small gauge—down to about 22 gauge without too much loss. On all transmitting applications, however, it pays to use high-quality coaxial cable—cable such as RG-8/U is recommended. Other coax has a greater loss factor and will diminish the signal by burning up energy in the form of heat.

The same applies to antenna tuners. For strictly receiving applications, antenna tuners can use tiny components without problems. However, if the antenna tuner is used for a transmitter it must be constructed of heavier components to prevent losses and arcing (spark discharge).

Lightning Protection

If any external antenna is used in weather active areas, it should be fitted with a lightning arrester, or provision should be made for disconnecting the antenna from the receiver and grounding it during thunderstorms. Lighting can extensively damage your equipment with even a nearby strike, and at the worst, can kill.

FOR YOUR OWN SAFETY

Avoid operating your receiving or transmitting equipment during electrical storms. Ground the two conductors of the lead-in wire directly to a good earth ground, such as a outside metallic water pipe (not a gas pipe) before electrical storms. This can be done by a heavy switch or temporary plug connector, as shown in Figure 11-12.

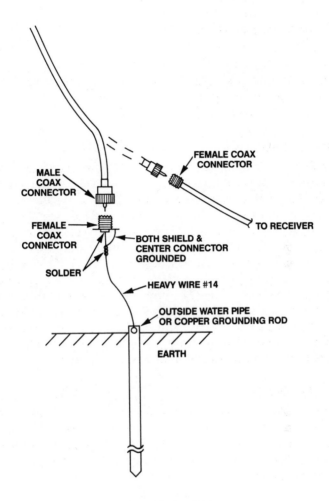

Figure 11-12.
Grounding an Antenna with Coax
Fittings

Section III
Glossary of Terms

The following is a list of commonly used terms pertaining to radio bands, receivers, scanners, simple antennas, operating practices, and radio stations.

Advanced class - Second highest class of radio amateur as far as privileges.

AF - Audio frequency. Frequencies in the range of 20 to 20,000 Hz. Those frequencies a person can hear.

aircraft band - (Usually) The band at 108—135 MHz dedicated to aircraft communications.

AM — Amplitude modulation. Commonly used way of transmitting voice or other signals with radio transmission. Used primarily on bands below 30 MHz.

AM broadcast band - The broadcast band from 550 kHz to 1600 kHz as used in the United States by commercial stations.

amateur radio - Radio and other types of communication between licensed radio amateurs (hams).

AMTOR - Amateur Teleprinting Over Radio. Type of RTTY used on lower-frequency ham bands.

analog receiver - Any receiver that tunes in stations by converting mechanical movement to a frequency change, as opposed to synthesized receiver.

antenna - A wire that transmits or receives radio waves.

antenna tuner - Device that matches the impedance of an antenna to the impedance of a receiver or transmitter.

ARRL - American Radio Relay League. De facto representative of radio amateurs.

autopatch - A communications link with the telephone lines.

aviation band - See aircraft band.

bandwidth - Total width of a radio signal, varying from a few hundred Hz for CW to five or six MHz for TV.

base station - A permanent transceiver (or transmitter), as opposed to a mobile station.

baud - A unit of signaling speed equal to one bit or event per second.

beat-frequency oscillator (BFO) - Internal receiver oscillator that enables reception of CW (code) and single-sideband signals.

beam - A directional antenna with several elements parallel to each other.

beacon - A radio transmitter running continuously and marking a navigational aid, frequency, or satellite.

BFO - See beat frequency oscillator.

carrier frequency - The unmodulated frequency of a radio signal.

CB - See Citizen's Band.

CBer - A Citizen's Band operator.

Channel - Predetermined frequency, sometimes given a number for easy reference.

CHU - Canadian time and frequency station.

Citizen's Band - Usually the band at about 27 MHz, which has been set aside for two-way communication for the general public. Also, numerous other bands at different frequencies.

clarifier - An incremental tuning control for reception of SSB signals, especially on CB transceivers.

clear-channel station - An AM broadcast band radio station that shares its channel only with distant stations.

coax - See coaxial cable.

coaxial cable - A two-conductor, shielded cable used for radio frequencies.

code - Communication by (usually) International Morse code.

common carrier - A telephone company.

communications receiver - Any receiver designed to receive CW, single sideband, and AM with high quality.

converter - A device that converts one frequency band to another frequency band.

crystal filter - Electronic circuit for receivers designed to produce high selectivity by quartz crystal use.

crystal set - Simple radio receiver employing a crystal detector.

CW - Continuous wave. (Usually) code transmission.

dB - See decibel.

decibel (dB) - Smallest detectable change in audio level. Used also to measure electrical signals.

digipeater - A repeater used for packet radio.

digital receiver - A synthesized receiver.

dipole antenna - Simple half-wavelength, center-fed antenna.

down converter - A converter whose output is a lower frequency.

down link - A rebroadcast from a satellite.

DTMF pad - Dual-Tone Multi-Frequency pad. A circuit that permits telephone dial tones to be generated. Widely used in VHF and UHF transceivers for scanner use.

DX - Radio abbreviation for distance.

DXer - A ham or shortwave listener who attempts to hear or communicate with distant stations.

ECPA - The Electronics Communication Privacy Act of 1986.

effective radiated power (ERP) - The transmitter power actually radiated by the antenna system.

EHF - Extremely high frequencies in the range of 30 to 300 GHz.

ELF - Extremely low frequencies in the range of 30 to 300 Hz.

EPIRB - Emergency Position Indicating Radiobeacon. A VHF position indicator for emergencies.

ERP - See effective radiated power.

Extra Class - Highest class of radio amateur as far as privileges.

facsimile (fax) - A means of encoding, transmitting, and receiving pictures and photos.

fast-scan television - Normal television transmission, or adaptations by radio amateurs.

fax - See facsimile.

FCC - Federal Communications Commission. Regulatory agency for radio, television, and communications.

field-strength meter - A device that measures the strength of radio waves some distance from the transmitter.

filtering - In a receiver, removal or attenuation of unwanted signals by radio-frequency or audio-frequency filters.

FM - See frequency modulation.

FM band - The broadcast band from 88 to 108 MHz.

frequency calibrator - A device that transmits marker frequencies for calibration of receiving equipment.

frequency crystal - Quartz crystal that determines receiving or transmitting frequency in some receivers, transmitters, or transceivers.

frequency modulation (FM) - A modulation method in which the transmitter frequency is varied to represent the audio frequency to be sent. Used extensively on bands above 30 MHz.

FSK - Frequency shift keying. Modulation method for RTTY and other transmissions.

General class - Most common class of radio amateur.

GHz - Gigahertz. 1,000,000,000 Hz.

ground wave - Part of a radio transmission that follows the earth's curvature.

ham - See radio amateur.

ham band - A radio band allocated fully or partially to amateur use.

hand-held - Any small hand-held receiver or transceiver.

half-wave dipole - See dipole antenna.

headphone - Miniature audio speakers that fit closely over the ears for better hearing.

heterodyne - An audio beat note resulting from combining two close signals.

hertz (Hz) - One cycle per second of frequency.

HF - High frequencies in the range of 3 MHz to 30 MHz.

HT - Abbreviation for walkie-talkie. A hand-held transceiver.

International Morse Code - See Morse code.

ionosphere - Reflecting layer of ionized particles surrounding earth.

IRC - International Reply Coupon. A way of sending return postage internationally.

kHz - Kilohertz. 1000 Hz.

kW - Kilowatt. 1000 watts.

LCD display - Liquid crystal display. A low-power display common on scanners and other receivers.

LED display - A light-emitting diode display found on some scanners and receivers.

LF - Low frequencies in the range of 30 kHz to 300 kHz.

lightning arrester - A lightning protection device.

line-of-sight - Referring to maximum distance traveled by UHF and some VHF radio waves.

linear amplifier - Common type of transmitter amplifier that produces high-power radio signals.

long wave (LW) - The AM broadcast band used in Europe below the United States broadcast band at 148.5 - 183.5 MHz.

LORAN - Long Range Navigation system operating at 100 kHz.

LSB - In single-sideband transmission, the lower-frequency sideband selected to carry the audio information.

LW - See long wave.

marine band - (Generally) the VHF 156.050 to 157.425-MHz band that carries marine radio transmissions.

medium wave - The AM broadcast band (550 to 1600 kHz) as found in Europe or other countries.

meter - Basic unit of length in metric system. 39.37 inches.

MF - Medium frequencies in the range of 300 kHz to 3 MHz.

MHz - Megahertz. 1,000,000 Hz.

microvolt - One millionth of a volt. Usually used to specify radio signals at the antenna of a receiver.

microwave - Radio waves in the 1,000,000,000 Hz (1 GHz) range and above.

milliwatt - A thousandth of a watt.

mobile station - A transmitter/receiver in a car, truck, ship, or airplane.

modulation - A means of impressing audio or other information on a radio or television signal.

monaural - Sound originating from a single source, as opposed to stereo.

monophonic - Monaural.

Morse code - A way of transmitting information in which individual characters are encoded as a series of short and long signals.

MW - See medium wave.

narrow-band amplifier - A (usually) RF amplifier that amplifies only a narrow range of frequencies.

NBFM - Narrow-band frequency modulation. Occasionally used on the HF bands for frequency modulation.

ni-cad battery - A nickel cadmium rechargeable battery found in receivers, transceivers, and scanners and used to power the memory.

NOAA - National Oceanic and Atmospheric Administration. The national weather service agency.

noise - Random signals from internal (receiver) or natural sources.

notch filter - A receiver filter that suppresses unwanted signals.

Novice class - Lowest class of radio amateur as far as privileges.

OMEGA - LF navigation system used for submarine navigation and by the public.

OMNI - VHF navigation system used by aircraft.

OSCAR I - First amateur radio satellite, boosted to orbit in 1961.

overload - A signal that is too strong for a receiver and swamps the RF amplifier circuits.

packet radio - A communications method by which messages are sent in short bursts with error correction capability. Used by hams and others.

peak envelope power (PEP) - Method of measuring power of single-sideband transmitters.

PEP - See peak envelope power.

phased locked loop (PLL) - Used in receivers that synthesize frequencies for a stable signal.

phone patch - A transceiver connected to a telephone line for remote telecommunications.

pirate - An unauthorized radio or television broadcaster.

PL-259 - Common coaxial cable connector.

PLL - See phased locked loop.

portable phone - A wireless phone that is, in fact, a self-contained transmitter and receiver.

power - Energy over time. The power of a radio transmitter is measured in watts.

power supply - The electronics that (usually) convert ac power into the voltages needed in receivers or transmitters.

programmed scanner - See scanner.

propagation - The way radio waves travel around the world or locally.

QRP - Low-power amateur radio operation.

QSL card - A card sent by a shortwave station verifying that a listener has received the station. A similar card sent by a radio amateur.

radio amateur - (Or ham). An individual who has been licensed to operate a radio on certain frequencies for the purpose of enjoyment, technical training, and public service.

radio spectrum - The range of frequencies over which radio signals can be transmitted.

radiobeacon - A radio transmitter whose signals mark a location or navigational danger.

remote broadcast - A broadcast from remote site to radio or television studio.

repeater - A transceiver that rebroadcasts an incoming signal with greater power and/or wider range.

RF - Radio frequency.

RF gain control - A receiver control that determines the amplification in the RF section and used to prevent signal overloading.

RG-8U, RG-58U - Coaxial cable used in antenna lead-ins.

RIT - Receiver incremental tuning. A means to tune the receiver in a transceiver a short distance away from the current transmitter frequency.

RS-232-C - Standard computer interface that can be used with some receivers or transceivers.

RTTY - Radio teleprinting. See Teleprinter.

Rubber ducky - A short, flexible antenna for hand-held radios.

Russian woodpecker - Over-the-horizon radar that causes interference on shortwave bands.

S-meter - A meter on a receiver that indicates received signal strength.

scanner - A radio receiver, usually with coverage in the VHF or UHF regions that automatically scans a set or band of frequencies, stopping on active channels.

selectivity - The ability of a receiver to separate adjacent signals.

sensitivity - The ability of a receiver to receive weak signals.

SHF - Super high frequencies in the range of 3 GHz to 30 GHz.

shortwave - Radio waves in the region from 3 to 30 MHz.

sideband - An envelope about the carrier frequency of an AM or single-sideband signal that carries the audio-frequency information of the signal.

signal-to-noise ratio (SNR) - The ratio of received signal over the background noise, usually expressed in decibels.

single sideband (SSB) - Voice transmission with a narrower bandwidth than AM, enabled by eliminating the carrier and one sideband.

SINPO - A standard way of reporting reception to foreign broadcasters.

skip - The received signal of a radio transmission resulting from ionospheric reflection.

sky wave - The part of a radio wave that radiates away from the earth and is sometimes reflected back by the ionosphere.

slow-scan television - Television transmission with narrow enough bandwidth to be sent in the lower-frequency bands.

SNR - See signal-to-noise ratio.

solar flares - Disturbances on the sun that affect radio communications.

squelch - A circuit in a receiver that turns off the audio unless a signal is received.

SSB - See single sideband.

stability - The ability of a receiver to remain tuned to the selected frequency without change.

subband - Any further division of a radio band.

subcarrier - Supplemental information carried in a radio or television signal, such as background music or foreign language.

sun spot - Dark spot on the sun's surface affecting ionosphere and radio wave propagation.

sun spot cycle - 11-year cycle of sun spot activity determining radio conditions.

superheterodyne - Typical radio receiver circuit in which incoming signals are converted to an intermediate frequency for amplification.

SWL - A shortwave listener.

SWR Meter - An instrument that measures the match between antenna impedance and feedline impedance.

synthesized receiver - Any receiver that receives stations by reading a frequency from keys or switches and then digitally combines frequencies to arrive at the reception frequency.

Technician class - Class of radio amateur.

teleprinter - A machine or computer system that transmits and receives messages as a series of rapidly (100 words per minute typical) encoded characters.

transceiver - A transmitter and receiver in a single package, whether for commercial, military, Citizen's Band, or amateur use.

trapped antenna - A multi-band antenna, usually for amateur applications.

tropical broadcasting - Shortwave (or medium-wave) broadcasting in the earth's tropical regions.

TVRO - Television receive only. Reception of television broadcast over satellite links.

UHF - Ultra high frequencies in the range of 300 to 3000 MHz.

UHF television - Channels 14 through 83 of commercial television.

up converter - A converter whose output is a higher frequency than the input frequency.

up link - The frequency used to transmit to a satellite for rebroadcast.

USB - Upper sideband. In single-sideband transmission, the higher frequency sideband selected to carry the audio information.

UTC - Universal Time Code. A worldwide way of reporting time based on the time in Greenwich, England.

v antenna - A long-wire, high-gain antenna used on the HF band.

VCO - Voltage controlled oscillator. A way to generate oscillator signals in a synthesized receiver or transceiver.

vertical antenna - An antenna in which the radiating element is oriented in a vertical direction.

VF - Voice frequencies in the range of 300 Hz to 3 kHz.

VFO - Variable frequency oscillator. A tunable oscillator for generating an RF signal.

VHF - Very high frequencies in the range of 30 to 300 MHz.

VHF television - The commercial television channels 2 through 13.

VLF - Very low frequencies in the range of 3 to 30 kHz.

VOX - Voice operated switch. Usually used to automatically turn a transmitter on and off when the operator speaks.

walkie-talkie - Any small, portable (usually hand-held) transceiver.

watt - Unit of power.

wavelength - The length of a radio wave, usually expressed in meters.

weather radio - A radio receiver designed to receive NOAA weather broadcasts in the 162 MHz range.

whip antenna - A quarter-wave antenna used on mobile radios or hand-held units.

wide-band - An amplifier that is capable of amplifying a wide band of frequencies and does not need to be carefully tuned.

wireless phone - See portable phone.

WWV/WWVH - National Bureau of Standards time and frequency stations.

yagi antenna - A beam type of antenna, often used for TV.

Section IV
Appendices

Appendix I
Bibliography

Shortwave Listening

"World Radio TV Handbook", Billboard Ltd., Billboard Publications Inc., 1515 Broadway, New York 10036, NY. Master handbook of all shortwave broadcasters with frequencies, times, and other data. Equipment reviews as well. A must for SWLs.

"Radio Database International", International Broadcasting Service, Ltd., P.O. Box 300, Penn's Park, PA 18943. Handbook of shortwave broadcasters in chart format plus equipment reviews.

"Shortwave Listening Handbook", Harry L. Helms, Prentice-Hall, 1987. Excellent 246-page text on shortwave listening tips, techniques, equipment, and secrets.

Amateur Radio

"The ARRL 1987 Handbook for the Radio Amateur", ARRL, 1987, American Radio Relay League, Newington, CT 06111. The "bible" for all facets of ham radio. A massive volume containing theory and projects.

Antennas

"Antennas—Selection and Installation", Alvis J. Evans, Radio Shack 62-1083. Installation and use of CB and shortwave antennas, among others.

AM Broadcast Band

"White's Radio Log", Worldwide Publications. Listing of United States and Canadian AM and FM stations.

VHF and UHF Scanners

"Fox Scanner Radio Listings", Fox Marketing, Inc. 4518 Taylorsville Road, Dayton, OH 45424-2497. Listings of local VHF and UHF stations in every kind of order. Indispensable.

Communications Magazines

"Popular Communications", Popular Communications, Inc., 76 North Broadway, Hicksville, NY 11801. Monthly magazine with coverage of scanners, shortwave, pirates, clandestine operations, and other topics.

"QST", ARRL, American Radio Relay League, Newington, CT 06111. Construction projects, theory, and ARRL happenings.

"CQ", CQ Publishing, Inc., 76 North Broadway, Hicksville, NY 11801. Monthly amateur radio magazine. Construction projects, theory, reviews of equipment, and ham radio events.

"73 Magazine", WGE Publishing, WGE Center, Peterborough, NH 03458-1194. Monthly amateur radio magazine. Construction projects, theory, reviews of equipment, and interesting editorials.

Radio Projects

"Engineer's Mini-Notebook: Communications Projects", Forrest Mims III, Radio Shack 276-5015. An excellent compendium that includes do-it-yourself radio projects for the beginner.

Weather Satellites

"The New Weather Satellite Handbook", Ralph E. Taggart, WGE Publishing, WGE Center, Peterborough, NH 03458-1194. Excellent book on reception of weather satellite data with construction details.

Appendix II
International Morse Code

The table below lists common International Morse Code Characters. The timing between elements is as follows:

- One dot is the basic unit.
- A dash is three times the length of a dot.
- There is one dot length of time between the individual elements, for example, between the dash, dash, dot, and dot of Z.
- There are three dot lengths of time between individual letters, for example, between the "C", "A", and "T" of "CAT".
- There are seven dot lengths of time between individual words, for example between "THE", "CAT", and "IS" in the sentence starting "THE CAT IS . . .".

Letters

Letter	Code
A	.-
B	-...
C	-.-.
D	-..
E	.
F	..-.
G	--.
H	....
I	..
J	.---
K	-.-
L	.-..
M	--
N	-.
O	---
P	.--.
Q	--.-
R	.-.
S	...
T	-
U	..-
V	...-
W	.--
X	-..-
Y	-.--
Z	--..

Digits

0	-----
1	.----
2	..---
3	...--
4	....-
5	.....
6	-....
7	--...
8	---..
9	----.

Special Characters

period	.-.-.-
comma	--..--
? (question mark)	..--..
dash	-...-
slash	-..-.

Operating Characters

error	....
wait	.-...
end of message	.-.-.
go ahead	-.-
end of session	...-.-

Appendix III
Radio "Q" Signals

Radio Q signals are used as abbreviations either for asking a question or for a reply to a question. For example, an amateur might say "QSY up 10 kHz", meaning "Move up in frequency 10 kHz". Q signals are used by CB operators, amateurs, and commercial stations. "10" signals (Appendix IV) are often used in the VHF and UHF bands by police, fire, emergency services, and others.

Signal	Question	Response
QRG	What is my exact frequency?	Your exact frequency is --.
QRH	Does my frequency vary?	Your frequency varies.
QRI	How is my tone?	Your tone is (1-5; bad-good).
QRK	What is my readability?	You are readable (1-5;bad-good).
QRL	Are you busy?	I am busy.
QRM	Is there interference?	There is interference.
QRN	Is there static?	There is static.
QRO	Shall I increase power?	Increase power.
QRP	Shall I decrease power?	Decrease power.
QRQ	Shall I send faster?	Send faster at -- (wpm).
QRS	Shall I send more slowly?	Send more slowly at -- (wpm).
QRT	Shall I stop sending?	Stop sending.
QRU	Have you anything for me?	I have nothing for you.
QRV	Are you ready?	I am ready.
QRX	When will you call again?	At -- hours on -- frequency.
QSA	What is my signal strength?	Your strength is (1-5; bad-good).
QSB	Am I fading?	You are fading.
QSD	Are my signals defective?	Your signals are defective.
QSG	Shall I send -- messages?	Send -- messages at one time.
QSK	Do you have break in?	I have break in.
QSL	Will you acknowledge receipt?	I acknowledge receipt.
QSM	Shall I repeat the message?	Repeat the last (or --) message.
QSN	Did you hear me on --?	I heard you on -- (frequency).
QSO	Can you communicate with --?	I can communicate with --.
QSP	Will you relay to --?	I will relay to --.
QST	General call to ARRL members.	--
QSU	Shall I send on -- (freq.)?	Send on -- (frequency).
QSV	Shall I send a series of Vs?	Send a series of Vs.

QSW	Will you send on -- (freq)?	Send on -- (frequency).
QSX	Will you listen on -- (freq)?	I will listen on -- (frequency).
QSY	Shall I change to -- (freq)?	Change to -- (frequency).
QSZ	Shall I send each word group more than once?	Send each word group -- times.
QTA	Shall I cancel message --?	Cancel message --.
QTB	Do you agree with my word count?	I agree with your word count.
QTC	How many messages do you have?	I have -- messages.
QTH	What is your location?	My location is --.
QTR	What is the correct time?	The correct time is --.

Appendix IV
Radio "10" Signals

Radio 10 signals are used as abbreviations either for asking a question or for a reply to a question. For example, an ambulance dispatcher might ask "What is your 10-20?" and the reply might be "My 10-20 is near Main and 3rd". "10" signals are often used in the VHF and UHF bands by police, fire, emergency services, and others. Radio "Q" signals (Appendix III) are used in the MF and HF bands for two-way communication between amateurs, CB operators, and commercial stations. Often different services have different meanings for some of the less commonly used codes, so this list is a general guide only.

10-0	Caution	10-26	Detaining subject, expedite
10-1	Unable to copy, change location	10-27	Drivers license information
		10-28	Vehicle registration information
10-2	Signal good		
10-3	Stop transmitting	10-29	Check records for wanted or stolen
10-4	Ok, acknowledgement		
10-5	Relay	10-30	Unnecessary use of radio
10-6	Busy, unless urgent	10-31	Crime in progress
10-7	Out of service	10-32	Man with gun
10-8	In service	10-33	Emergency
10-9	Repeat	10-34	Riot
10-10	Fight in progress	10-35	Major crime alert
10-11	Dog case	10-36	Correct time
10-12	Stand by, stop	10-37	Investigate suspicious vehicle
10-13	Weather and road conditions	10-38	Stopping suspicious vehicle
10-14	Prowler report	10-39	Urgent, use light and siren
10-15	Civil disturbance	10-40	Silent run, no light or siren
10-16	Domestic problem	10-41	Beginning tour of duty
10-17	Meet complainant	10-42	Ending tour of duty
10-18	Complete assignment quickly	10-43	Information
10-19	Return to station or ...	10-44	Permission to leave ... for ...
10-20	Location	10-45	Animal carcass
10-21	Call ... by telephone	10-46	Assist motorist
10-22	Disregard	10-47	Emergency road repair
10-23	Arrived at scene	10-48	Traffic standard repair
10-24	Assignment completed	10-49	Traffic light out
10-25	Report in person, meet	10-50	Accident

10-51 Wrecker needed
10-52 Ambulance needed
10-53 Road blocked
10-54 Livestock on highway
10-55 Intoxicated driver
10-56 Intoxicated pedestrian
10-57 Hit and run
10-58 Direct traffic
10-59 Convoy or escort
10-60 Squad in vicinity
10-61 Personnel in area
10-62 Reply to message
10-63 Prepare to make written copy
10-64 Message for local delivery
10-65 Net message assignment
10-66 Message cancellation
10-67 Clear for net message
10-68 Dispatch information
10-69 Message received
10-70 Fire alarm
10-71 Advise nature of fire
10-72 Report progress of fire
10-73 Smoke report
10-74 Negative
10-75 In contact with . . .

10-76 En route to . . .
10-77 Estimated time of arrival
10-78 Need assistance
10-79 Notify coroner
10-80 Chase in progress
10-81 Breatherlizer report
10-82 Reserve lodging
10-83 Work school crossing at ...
10-84 If meeting ... advise ETA
10-85 Delayed due to ...
10-86 Officer/operator on duty
10-87 Pick up/distribute checks
10-88 Present telephone number
        of . . .
10-89 Bomb threat
10-90 Bank alarm
10-91 Pick up prisoner/subject
10-92 Improperly parked vehicle
10-93 Blockade
10-94 Drag racing
10-95 Prisoner/subject in custody
10-96 Mental subject
10-97 Check signal
10-98 Prison/jail break
10-99 Wanted or stolen indicated

NOTES

NOTES

NOTES